Science in colour

Ron Adams

Stanley Thornes (Publishers) Ltd

Introduction

This book aims to provide you with a substantial bank of visual inspiration and ideas for science in your school. It is organised to coincide with the National Curriculum structure for science while investigations are provided throughout the book as a regular feature. In a similar way, learning objectives associated with the activities punctuate each section of the book.

Within the different areas of science, activities are usually structured as either 'First activities' for younger children, or 'Further activities' for older or more advanced children.

Everything in this book has been tried and tested with children in real classroom situations.

Our aim throughout this book has been to provide you with inspiration for teaching science in a creative and stimulating environment.

Acknowledgements

The author and publisher would like to thank the children and staff of the following Wiltshire schools for their generous help in making this book possible:
Westlea CP, Swindon (Head Neil Griffiths), Windmill Hill CP, Swindon (Head Dave Messenger and Deputy Mark Hazzard), Walwayne Court CP (Head Richard Brown, Deputy Jackie Holton, Julia Hawkins, Madelin Matthews, Helen Waters, Rebecca Gregory, Ceri Mee, Joanne Woodhouse, Barbara Smith and Jo French), Box Highlands (Head Mike Plummer), Melksham Lowbourne Junior (Head Sue Johnson, also thanks to Carola Cooper), Devizes Wansdyke Junior (Head James Smith and Jacqui Monckton), Colerne Primary (Head Jo Stone and Jenny Elvin), St. Stephen's Primary, Bath (Head Veronica Parker and Mrs. Swan).

Thanks are also due to Mike Chislett, General Primary Consultant, Wiltshire County Council, Spiros and Socrates Adams-Florou for the wordsearches and a number of pieces of science artwork.

'Winter Morning' by Ogden Nash is reprinted by permission of Curtis Brown Ltd. Copyright © 1962 by Ogden Nash, renewed.

Contents

Life processes - living things

Materials

Physical processes

Life processes –

First activities

1 Are toys alive?

Encourage the children to bring in toys to class. Discuss whether or not the soft toys are alive. Ask questions about the toys such as: Do they breathe? Can they run around? Do they eat? What sort of food do they like? Make drawings and tell stories.

2 Class pet book

Make a class book of what happens to the class pet. Get the children to note how it moves, eats and when it has babies. Take photographs and make drawings as evidence. Make a list of the things that pets do and what they look like.

3 Plant search

Find from your school grounds three or four small plants and use reference books to name them. Make detailed drawings of them and write down observed similarities and differences. Grow some seeds in egg box plant pots, as shown.

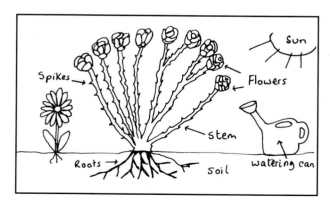

4 Macdonald's Farm

Use a cut away cardboard box as corner display, paint clouds and fields in place. Get children to make small animals from Plasticine or art maché. Write the names of the animals on labels with the sounds they make.

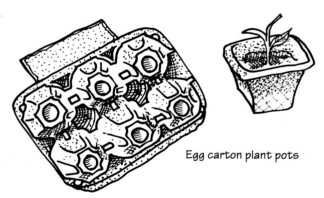

Egg carton plant pots

4

Life processes -

First activities

1 Drought study
Collect pictures of droughts and examine the impact that the lack of water has on landscape, vegetation, people and animals. Discuss how important water is for all living things.

2 Lively friends
Act as a scribe, or get a helper to record what the children observe each other doing in their everyday lives. Try to encourage them to use words such as *move, feed, breathe* and *grow*. Extend this activity to make a weekly diary of what they do and include dance activities such as jumping, crawling, sliding, turning, being still.

3 Identity parade quiz
Each child can make a careful, reasonably sized (20cm X 10cm) drawing of a specific animal, object or plant. Do not label them but use them as part of a quiz.

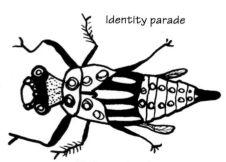

Identity parade

Find out what I am

Try this investigation

School safari: Take the children around the school buildings and grounds looking for: school pets, ladybirds, spiders and their webs, woodlice and all kinds of small land and pond creatures. Keep notes about where they live and how they move. Choose two animals for close examination. Draw them, identifying similarities and differences between them. Then make a map of your school (see illustration), including all the areas in which the small creatures were found.

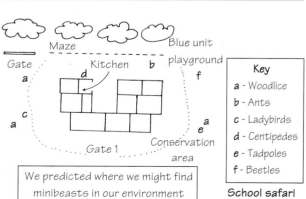

We predicted where we might find minibeasts in our environment

Maze
Gate
Kitchen
Blue unit playground
Gate 1
Conservation area

Key
a - Woodlice
b - Ants
c - Ladybirds
d - Centipedes
e - Tadpoles
f - Beetles

School safari

living and non-living

Further activities

1 Sorting living and non-living things
Collect together a variety of objects. Discuss with the children how they can classify things as either *living* or *non-living* (inanimate) according to basic life processes. Extend this activity to classify using three groups: animals, plants and inanimate things.

2 What my nose can do
Ask the children to write down the various senses and then use these to draft a story which is entitled: *What my eyes, ears, nose, tongue and fingers can do*. Make a concertina book with pictures to illustrate each little section.

Try this investigation

Signs of life: Get the children to try to stimulate some kind of reaction such as movement or other signs of response from a stone or other inanimate object. Get them to record their observations and report them to the class. Discuss whether or not inanimate things (e.g. stones, metal tubes, felt tip pens) have any feelings or the ability to move around by themselves. What are authentic signs of life?

3 'Animal, vegetable or mineral'
Organise a class game with an award for the winning team. Each team chooses a subject which then has to be guessed by the others. Twenty questions can be answered only with 'yes' or 'no' and the only clues given at the beginning are to do with the categories of the objects.

Life processes -

First activities

1 Noah's animals

Make a visit to the zoo where children observe and make sketches of animals. Back in class, talk about similarities and differences between animals. Then choose some animals that were in Noah's Ark and ask the children to make a wall display of the Ark with the animals (use books).

2 How do they grow?

Discuss how different creatures reproduce, and make comparative posters for different creatures showing their life cycles. Try frogs, stick insects, snails, ladybirds and hens. To extend this activity, incubate some chicks. Make records of school pets, weigh them over a period of time and make simple graphs of "how our pet grows". Make displays of young and adult animals.

3 Conservation area map and key

Discuss how simple keys can be made so that people can identify living things easily. Make a map of the school's conservation area and include a key to show the different varieties of plant and animal life found. To extend this activity, cut out all kinds of creatures from magazines and sort them according to different criteria such as size, colour, number of legs, etc.

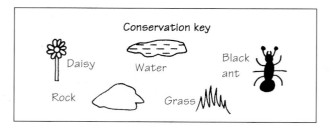

Conservation key

Daisy · Water · Black ant · Rock · Grass

Try to grow

An avocado stone: Insert three pins around the middle of the avocado stone and stand it on a jam jar full of water (as in illustration). After a few days the children can observe the formation of roots. When the top has sprouted transfer the avocado into a pot.

A potato: Leave the potato in a shady dry place until it forms 2-3 little roots, then put it in a pot filled with compost and water.

A pineapple plant: Turn the leafy top of a pineapple with your hands until it is removed. Insert the bottom of the leafy top in compost and watch it grow.

A spider plant: Take some baby plants, immerse in water as shown below, then place in potting compost and water them.

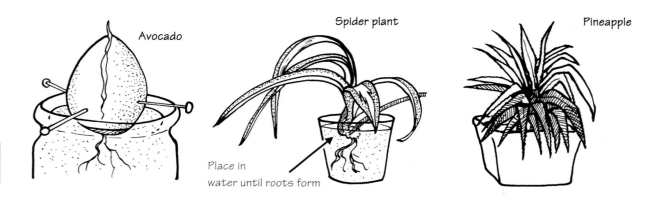

Avocado

Spider plant

Place in water until roots form

Pineapple

similar and different

Further activities

1 Identifying species

Talk about the many ways that different species can be categorised, for example, by habitat or by diet (herbivorous or carnivorous). Get some examples of the teeth of pigs, sheep and a dog to examine at first hand. Cut out from magazines many different kinds of creatures and ask the children to sort them out by diet using Venn diagrams. Ask them to choose one other way to sort them out.

2 Animal homes

Choose two different environments in the school grounds. Ask the children to predict what kind of animals will be living in those two environments (such as under bark chippings or stones). Use data collection sheets and find out what creatures do live there. Ask children to compare their findings with their predictions.

Try this investigation

Leaf lengths: Collect samples (ten each) of different leaves such as: beach leaves, oak leaves and mallow bush leaves. Use calculators, tape measures, rulers, pencils and clipboards. Get the children to measure ten different leaves of the same variety and write down the measurements on a data collection sheet. Use the data to produce a line graph. Once completed, use the calculator to find the average length and then produce a drawing using the average dimensions.

3 Fruit and plant reproduction

Bring into the class various fruits. Cut them in half, study the cross-sections and seeds. Talk about seed distribution, germination and reproduction. Make detailed studies of the cross sections as in the photograph below.

Ourselves

Learning objectives

- Body parts have names.
- Different body parts are used for different activities.
- The skeleton provides support for the body.
- Joints provide movement for the skeleton.
- Muscles enable body movement.
- The heart pumps blood around the body.
- Body parts have specific functions.

First Activities

1 Identify external body parts

Work in pairs and draw body outlines of partners. Then label the head, arms, shoulders, neck, hands, legs and feet. Then ask the children to draw a labelled portrait of their partner.

2 Skeleton poem

Talk about the parts of the skeleton and the importance of having a strong support for our body. Make notes of words such as *strong, floppy, soft, hard, move,* etc. Make a drawing of a human skeleton and ask the children to write a poem about what the skeleton does.

3 What my body can do

Working in pairs, and with the aid of a helper, children can observe which parts of the body are used for particular actions or jobs e.g. when picking up a object. Simple prediction and recording actions can be followed. Other activities could include using the body in PE and to music.

4 Body parts

This series of activities helps children to name and identify body parts. Use articulated skeletons and play games such as 'Simon says'. Get the children to invent a doll's X-ray machine. Use feely bags with dolls inside: which part are you feeling now?

What my body can do

Doll's X ray machine

our bodies

Further activities

1 Model body with key
Use white cardboard to produce three sections through the human torso, the first to show the shoulder blades and back ribs, the second to show the spinal column and skull and the third to show the front ribs. Follow the illustration to assemble the torso.

2 Position of human organs
Working in pairs ask the children to draw around their partners on a large piece of paper or card to give a body shape. Use reference books to draw the following organs into position at the correct size and shape: the heart, lungs, stomach, kidneys and liver. Then label the organs.

3 Hidden words puzzle
Photocopy the word quiz and give out to the children. List of hidden human body words: *brain, heart, lungs, liver, kidneys, fingers, eyes, nose, mouth, ears, hair, elbow, knee cap, shoulders, arms, hands, toes, nails, teeth, tongue, wrist, bones, skull, shoulder blades, rib cage, blood, veins, blood vessels, chin, neck, heel, feet, ankle, pelvis, torso, tendons, navel, backbone, spine, back, knuckles, palm, skin, biceps, gum, lip, throat, intestines, vertebra, cells, eardrum, valve, joints.*

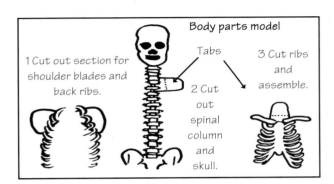

Body parts model

1 Cut out section for shoulder blades and back ribs.

Tabs

2 Cut out spinal column and skull.

3 Cut ribs and assemble.

B	A	R	N	E	Y	A	N	D	F	R	I	E	N	D	S	A	E	P	L	A	Y	M	N
U	O	Y	E	M	R	A	B	E	E	P	I	W	I	T	H	V	A	B	C	D	F	E	G
N	B	T	S	L	S	E	N	I	T	S	E	T	N	I	L	L	A	V	B	D	G	B	I
B	E	I	I	L	K	T	B	L	O	O	D	L	B	A	N	E	N	N	I	E	V	C	H
X	S	R	C	R	S	N	R	B	L	O	O	D	V	E	S	S	E	L	S	B	T	H	J
V	R	T	C	E	S	P	A	T	O	E	S	E	E	I	V	O	C	T	N	I	H	Z	L
E	V	E	U	P	P	I	M	V	R	S	I	A	R	C	S	N	K	O	A	C	R	J	K
I	T	P	R	T	T	L	S	T	E	N	A	R	T	A	D	I	F	E	I	E	O	B	N
N	T	S	S	S	A	N	N	V	S	L	I	V	E	R	V	H	E	A	L	P	O	N	M
N	K	O	I	P	S	H	O	U	L	D	E	R	B	L	A	D	E	S	S	S	T	P	P
N	S	C	S	R	I	D	D	J	E	A	R	D	R	U	M	Y	T	E	S	T	L	A	O
S	P	V	A	R	W	N	N	O	V	R	Z	C	A	H	E	G	H	N	L	Y	Y	N	R
B	A	C	K	B	O	N	E	I	S	I	T	H	Y	S	V	W	Z	X	I	U	I	C	Q
V	C	A	I	N	G	T	T	N	H	B	E	I	V	R	S	F	Y	V	U	K	K	R	T
S	E	L	C	T	U	M	Y	T	O	C	E	N	I	M	E	S	U	S	S	I	S	E	S
V	E	A	R	S	M	C	X	S	U	A	T	A	R	B	R	A	I	N	S	D	S	S	V
E	N	M	O	U	T	H	K	V	L	G	H	A	N	D	S	A	T	L	U	N	G	S	U
E	K	T	O	N	G	U	E	L	D	E	L	B	O	W	W	R	T	R	A	E	H	H	X
E	Y	N	C	E	L	L	S	R	E	G	N	I	F	B	R	I	A	N	N	Y	Y	S	W
I	V	S	S	L	E	S	N	V	R	S	N	F	B	C	E	L	L	E	C	S	S	X	Z
N	M	U	M	N	I	V	I	E	S	G	S	I	C	E	C	C	L	L	E	S	S	Z	Y

11

First activities

1 All my little flowers

Ask children to make their self-portraits. Cut them out and frame them in sunflower petals cut from tissue paper and stuck on yellow coloured card. Secure the flowers on stems made from green canes and then plant the flowers in a pot as shown in the photograph.

2 Funny bones

Play "Fossils" from *The Carnival of Animals* by Saint-Saens and ask the children what they can hear the skeletons doing. Get them to make pictures of their skeletons and add captions as shown in the photograph below.

3 Card print skeletons

Get the children to cut out pieces of card to represent the following body parts: hair, arms, torso, legs, hands and feet. Use these as printing plates, print on black paper with white paint, as below.

Further activities

1 Happy families

Ask the children to read the *Happy Families* stories by Allan Ahlberg. Children can use their favourite character (or family) from the books such as Mr Creepy, Miss Jump, Mrs Lather, Mr Tick the teacher, The Brick family, etc. Get the children to make their versions using Artisan software, as in the photograph.

2 Feet detectives

Get all children to draw around their bare feet on a piece of paper, using fine black felt-tip pens. Write their names in the corner on the back of the paper. Collect them all together and choose one secretly. Cut the corner off and keep the name somewhere safe. The children's job is to act as detectives and find whose foot matches the outline.

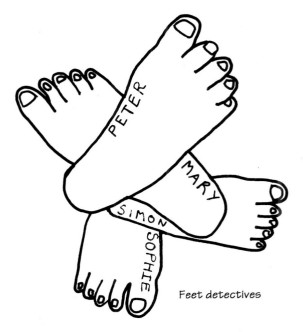

Feet detectives

13

Ourselves - similarities

First activities

1 What we all need

Discuss with the children what the basic life processes are. List them and ask children to write about them and make an illustrated *My body* book.

2 Animal family

From magazines cut out lots of pictures with different animals including human beings of various races. Discuss with the children about the similarities they can find between them, such as eating, breathing, moving, etc.

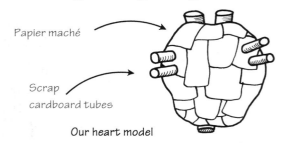

Papier maché

Scrap cardboard tubes

Our heart model

Learning objectives

- There are similarities and differences between humans and other animals.
- There are similarities and differences between humans.

Further activities

1 Blood

Discuss that we all have blood, whilst there are a number of common types of blood. Do the children know their blood groups? Use reference books, find out as many facts about blood as possible and the importance of blood to the body. Make up a blood display, adding information as it is found.

2 Our heart

Use reference books, junk materials and paper maché to make a 3D model of the heart with cut away sections. Link the heart to the respiratory system.

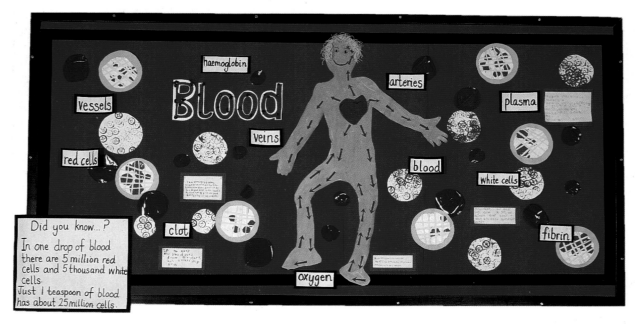

and differences

First activities

1 Class survey

Make a class survey recording the colour of eyes and hair and the height of the children. Use this data to produce simple bar charts. Keys for the various elements in the graph can be designed and colour coded.

2 Animal differences

Use the same magazine pictures as in Activity 2 on the previous page, but this time examine the differences between the different animals including humans.

Further activities

1 Four views

Working in pairs, the children faithfully record their partner's features. They can use drawings, paintings, photographs, clay modelling and written descriptions. Use all these media in a display, as shown above, to show the variety that exists in the class.

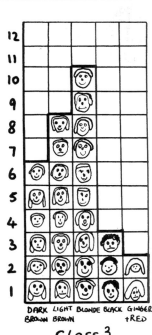

Look at this graph

Can you answer these questions?

1. How many children have black hair?

2. How many children have light brown hair?

3. Which colour is the most common?

4. There are only 2 children with _____ hair.

5. Can you work out how many children are in class 3?

15

Ourselves -

First activities

1 What can you hear?

Talk about the kind of sounds that can be heard in different places. Take the class into the playground and record the noises that can be heard. Play them back in class and identify them. How do these sounds compare with those heard at home or in a church? What sort of sounds do animals make? Children can choose their favourite sounds, illustrate, label and display them (see photograph).

2 Ear drawing

Ask children to make careful studies of a friend's ear. Ask questions such as: Why are ears shaped like that? Do all animals have ears? Why do some animals need big ears? Are ears only used for hearing?

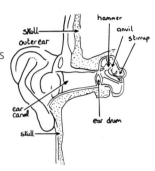

Try this investigation

Transmitting sound: Use electrical wires, buzzers and batteries to make a simple sound transmitting machine.

Further activities

1 How the ear works

If possible, get hold of an old wind-up gramophone, a large conch type shell or/and a simple megaphone. Use them to show how sound is collected by the ear, so that it reflects the sound to hit the ear drum. Get the children to use scrap materials such as small cardboard boxes, tubes and tissue paper to make their own models of how the ear works.

the senses

First activities

1 Eye words
Make a list of all the words that children can think of to do with eyes. Write them on labels and stick them on collage pictures of different coloured eyes that the children make (see below).

2 All the better to see you with
Tell the story of *Little Red Riding Hood*. The children have to design a pair of binoculars, glasses or other seeing device to detect wolves in grannies' clothing.

3 Blindfold
Work in pairs. Blindfold one child who uses one hand to touch the partner's face and using pastels, with the other hand, draws with soft, smooth, silky and sharp marks to represent the different parts of the head and face.

4 Feely pictures
Write down some words about touch, such as *smooth, soft, furry, hard, bumpy.* Get the children to use sorted scrap materials to make some pictures that are fun to touch. Make hand prints.

Try this investigation

In hot water: This group investigation shows how humans use their senses to be aware of the world around them. Explain the investigation to the children and encourage them to predict what will happen. Record their predictions.
Blindfolded, the children simultaneously put one hand in warm water and the other hand in cold water for two minutes. Then they put both hands in warm water. Review what happens and compare with predictions.

Learning objectives

- Humans use their senses to be aware of the world around them.
- Many everyday things have interesting textures.
- Noses and tongues are both important to the sense of taste.
- Different colours affect us differently.
- Our eyes sometimes play tricks on us.

Further activities

1 Braille notice
Discuss how eyes, ears, fingers, the tongue and the nose all give us information about the world. How can blind people be given information without the use of sound? Design and make notices that could be used blindfold. Make textured pictures.

First activities

1 Nosy picture

Paint profile portraits of friends. Write down words to describe different nose types, for example - *roman* and *aquiline*. Make a list of words to do with smell and things that we like to smell. Include these in a display with strong smelling things such as: garlic, orange, deodorant and even some socks!

2 Name that smell

Blindfold groups of children and pass around containers of strongly smelling items for them to try to identify. Include some fruit juice, spices, flowers and water.

3 World of smells

Ask the children to bring in different types of spices and herbs and plot them onto a map of the world. This could be linked to a topic on famous journeys.

Try this investigation

Smell this: Pairs of children smell sealed pots with holes in the lids of labelled as A, B, C, D, E: curry powder, vinegar, chocolate, coffee and tea. Get the children to name the substances or categorise them as good, bad or sour. Record results in a simple table.

Further activities

1 Favourite smell survey

Ask children to write down their three favourite smells. Collect the lists and get a group of children to produce tally charts to find out the most popular smells. Use this information to produce a class poster featuring a bar graph of the ten most popular smells.

the senses

First activities

1 Taste categories

Have a class discussion about tastes such as salty, sweet, sour, bitter. Encourage children to make a list of foods with different tastes. Talk about foods with more than one taste (e.g. sweet and sour).

Further activities

1 Lemon tastes like...

Get the children to write a description of what lemon tastes like. This can be followed by a written description of something tasting completely different such as chocolate.

2 Perfume

Extend the favourite smell activity on page 18 by asking the children to describe what their favourite perfume would smell of. They can then design and make the perfume (try crushing petals and mixing with water), the packaging, name and decorative label.

Try this investigation

Taste and smells: Blindfold the children and experiment with tasting different foods. Cut three or four cubes of apple, pear, cucumber and a strong smelling and tasting cheese. Having tasted them once, try again holding the nose. What difference was there? Do noses help us taste?

3 How we wrote our poems

Children go to the school garden, sit down in the quiet and note what they can see (with their eyes), hear (with their ears), smell (with their noses), touch (with their hands) and write down how they feel (sad, calm). Back in the class, children use these words and phrases to write a few sentences. Ask them to copy each sentence onto a strip of paper, look at it, decide which to keep for their poem and put the sentences in order they want to form their poem. Encourage children to look at ways of improving the sentences by using a thesaurus and discussion with other classmates. When all that is done, children choose titles for their poems and write the complete poems neatly. They can use the computer to print out them out. Finally, children can make drawings to express their poems. To extend the activity each child can produce the *How we wrote our poems* book to describe the various stages of the activity and the poem.

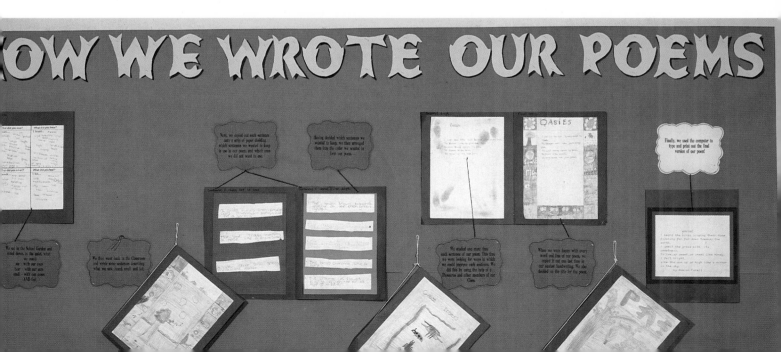

Ourselves -

First activities

1 Keeping healthy
Hold a class discussion about the main things we need to do in order to keep healthy, e.g. eat fresh fruit and vegetables, take exercise, don't eat too many sweets, fatty foods, sugar, etc. Children can draw pictures of their favourite activities and use them for a display.

2 Looking at fruit
Bring in different kinds of fruit and cut them in half. Ask the children to observe and make detailed drawings of the inside of the fruit and to write about them (see photograph below).

3 Food glorious food
Play the song from *Oliver* and discuss how food is digested and which kinds of food aid digestion. Write out phrases from the song and link these with detailed drawings of various glorious foods and of the digestive system of human beings.

4 Food display
Divide a large piece of red paper into 2x5 squares with strips of green paper. Help the children to make different kinds of food and place them on the squares. Try: an ice-cream cone, sausages (stuffed stockings), strawberries, jam tarts, bananas, crisps, grapes, beans, carrots and buns.

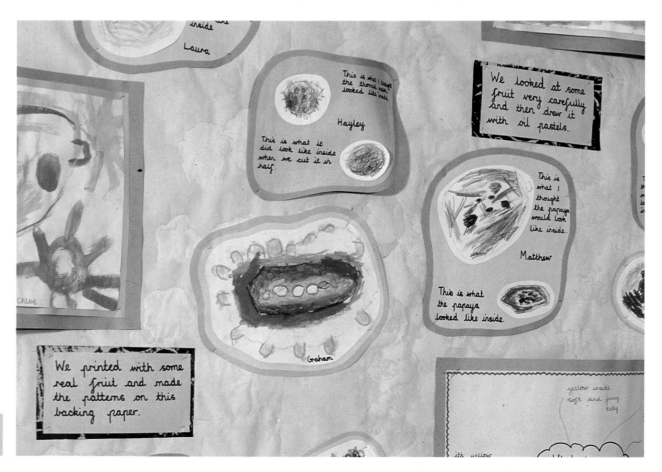

being healthy

Further activities

1 You are what you eat
Talk about food and the human digestive system. Cut a human figure (child's size) out of black paper and, using reference books, cut and stick in place the parts of the digestive system from different coloured paper.

2 Food categories

Ask the children to record what they ate yesterday and list the food under the main categories. Talk about food which is good for us and food which could harm us. Introduce the idea of a balanced diet.

3 Health matters charter
Discuss health issues including: asthma, smoking at home, amount of TV watched a day, books read, exercise, sleep, food eaten (fruit and vegetables versus crisps and sweets). Make a class charter of Do's and Don'ts.

4 My food takes a trip

Children draw the digestive system and write about the trip of their favourite food, beginning from the mouth.

Learning objectives

- Food and drink are essential for humans to live.
- Some foods give us energy.
- Eating sugary foods is bad for teeth.
- Exercise helps people stay healthy and strong.
- Humans eat meat, vegetables and fruit.
- Being overweight or underweight is not healthy.
- A varied diet is needed to stay healthy.
- Food needs to be digested before the body can use it.
- Breathing rates change with exercise.
- The pulse rate changes with exercise.
- Tobacco, alcohol and drugs can be harmful.

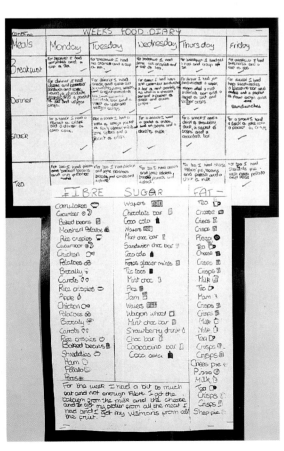

Ourselves - healthy and safe

First activities

1 Family tree
Get children to bring photographs of themselves and members of their families. Arrange them in groups to form little family trees. In class discussion ask the children: What do babies need to grow up healthy? How will children look when they grow old? (Children can make self-portraits of themselves as old people and compare with family photos.) Talk about human reproduction and growing up. Include children's comments in the family tree display.

2 Bath time for baby
Arrange to have a baby brought into class. Ask children how they would bath a baby. Write their comments in cut out yellow ducks and mount these with children's drawings of bath time and photographs of babies having a bath. Do some bubble prints. Extend this activity, comparing the conditions needed to sustain plant and human life, (stress how important water is to both). Make a simple comparative chart.

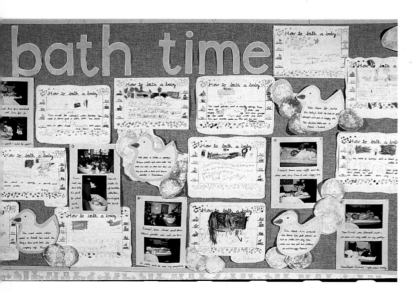

3 Water fun
Following on from the bath time activity, get the children to paint pictures of ways of enjoying water. To make a display, place the children's pictures around a central feature of a child playing in water. Add words and phrases such as *Jumping in, Puddles, Squirting, Floating and Sinking*. This activity can be extended (see page 41).

4 Teeth
One of the changes children notice most is how their teeth change. Talk about teeth and make up labels of some of the words that come up in discussion. Emphasise the need to look after teeth and ask children to make posters to encourage others to look after their teeth.

Further activities

1 Tooth survey
Get the children to make a survey of how often their class mates clean their teeth and how many fillings they have. Present the data in a simple bar graph.

2 Protect your body
Get children to draw pictures to show how to protect themselves against sunburn and cold weather. Get them to explain what is happening in their pictures.

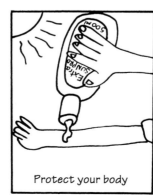

Protect your body

Ourselves - display ideas

1 Finding out about bread

Collect wrappers and packaging from bread (such as Hovis) and flour. Some supermarkets may have posters on breads. Examine and record the ingredients used in bread. Ask questions such as: What is vinegar used for? What are the additives? Are they necessary? How did our ancestors make bread? Try to get some samples of different cereals. Make a visit to a mill or grind your own flour.

2 Letters to Bertie

Get some children to write letters to Bertie the baker asking for information about bread and baking. Other children can act as Bertie to research and write back with drawings and recipes for breads and buns. Then the class can try out some of the recipes and taste the results, noting their opinions.

3 Spice adds variety to life

Draw upon the children's own cultures and talk about various foods. As an example, collect recipes of Indian food and make a class book that describes foods found in different geographical areas, the use of spices, ways of cooking and preserving food. Discuss the importance of food safety: the need to wash our hands before eating, to wash food well, to handle food carefully and to cook certain foods. Stress how important clean water is to health.

Try this investigation

Fermenting: Ask children questions such as: What makes bread dough rise? What do they think will happen when sugar and yeast are mixed in a bottle containing warm water? Try it as an experiment and put a balloon over the neck of the bottle. Watch what happens. Ask children to record the results and explain what happened.

4 Bertie Bun's Bakery Display

Good bread is an important element of our everyday diet. As part of work focusing on baking, you can produce a hands-on display of Bertie's bakery as shown in the photograph. You will need baker's hats, jackets, some dry wheat, bread tins, price lists of products, price tags, books about bread and yeast. The classroom corner bakery can be completed with various props such as a till, pretend money, a telephone and tiled wallpaper with flowery border.

Living things - plants

First activities

1 Name the plant parts
Talk about and study flowering plants. Get the children to use reference books and make detailed diagrams of flowering plants labelling their parts including definitions and information about plant life cycles.

2 Comparing
Choose two or three flowering plants. Observe them and compare their petals, leaves and stems. Draw them and write how they compare.

3 Bertie Bee
Make a pollination cartoon. Divide a piece of A4 paper into 6 or 8 sections. In each section draw an episode of Bertie Bee's life with captions such as: 'Mr. Bertie Bee flies towards a flower'.

4 Bean diary
Grow four bean plants. Keep perfect conditions for two: water them, keep warm in a light position and use good quality soil. Keep one plant in the dark (in a box), while all other conditions are kept perfect. Stop watering one plant while all other conditions are kept perfect. Ask the children to predict what will happen. Observe what happens over a period of time and record the results. Keep a diary of all stages of the experiment.

The final diary entry may read: *"Date...Two pots with perfect conditions: The beanstalks are looking healthy and are still growing. Pot with no water: Nothing has happened."*

5 Seeds and dispersal

Use reference books to find out how different plants reproduce and how their seeds are dispersed. Look at coconuts, dandelions, cherries and grass seeds found around the school. Talk about the importance of animals in seed dispersal - how some carry seeds in their coats whilst birds often carry seeds far from the parent plants.

Learning objectives

- Plants have different parts with different names.
- Seasons affect the growth of plants.
- Plants are found in a huge variety of different types.
- Plants can be sorted.
- Keys can be used to classify plants.
- Plants need sunlight and food to grow.
- Temperature affects how plants grow.
- The leaf, stem, root and flower have particular functions in plants.
- Green plants make their own food.
- Plants have a life cycle.
- Plants disperse their seeds in different ways and can germinate in a variety of ways.

Try these investigations

What do plants need?: Use a rubber plant. Cover one leaf completely and part of its stem. Place the plant near a window and observe what happens to it. A week later uncover the leaf and write what you think happened to it. Afterwards discuss with children the process of photosynthesis and how light is essential for green plants to produce their own food.

The frequency of plants: Get the children to throw hoops of regular size randomly in the school field. Count and identify the plants in each hoop. Use this data to calculate the frequency of each variety of wild plant in your field.

Stems: Place some carnations or daffodils in coloured water. Observe what happens and explain any effects by drawing diagrams.

Further activities

1 Sorting plants

Cut out pictures of plants from gardening magazines and then use Venn diagrams to sort the plants according to colour, shape and size.

Living things - plants

First activities

1 Comparing life cycles
Discuss how ladybirds lay eggs and flowering plants produce seeds which then produce new organisms. Use flowering plant seeds and monitor the progress of growth while you simultaneously observe a ladybird life cycle. Make a class posters for the two life cycles.

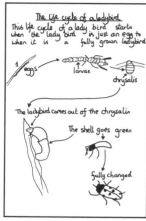

2 Practical gardening
Propagate plants from cuttings and baby plants. Take a cutting from a busy lizzy or use small spider plants from the mother plants. Immerse in water, note the date, height, colour of plants etc. Record progress regularly over a period of time.

3 Nursery visit
Visit a local garden centre or nursery, brainstorm about the different ways plants germinate. Try to germinate tomatoes, cress, beans and lettuce seeds.

Further activities

1 A gardener's world
Study a small area of the school grounds noting the position of the sun and any variations in the soil. Plan a garden choosing the seeds and plants for the different positions. Make drawings of full grown plants for their garden.

Try this
Discuss the necessary conditions for plant survival. Use six or seven similar plants, some in different types of soil, one in the cold, some drying on cotton wool, some fed and some in darkness. Monitor the progress of growth, and draw conclusions.

2 Spring in the garden
Get the children to make drawings and diagrams of spring flowers paying careful attention to leaf shapes and accurate colouring.

3 Flower stencils
Analyse the shapes of flowers and leaves and make a simplified drawing on a piece of thin card. Modify the drawing (see illustration) to produce a stencil that can then be used to decorate a Spring in the garden display.

4 Monet's garden
Use some of Monet's paintings as a starting point to discuss the suitability of plants to different environments. Monet's garden in Giverny, which took him 20 years to create, provided him with various subjects for painting. Seasonal changes in a garden can be shown by looking at some of his pictures.

5 *Tom's midnight garden*
Read the story and get the children to make their own version as an illustrated class book (see illustration below).

Making a stencil

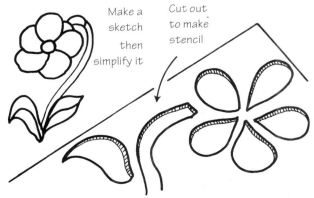

Make a sketch then simplify it

Cut out to make stencil

First activities

1 Seasons and plant growth

Make a record of seasonal activity of a suitable plant, shrub or tree near the classroom. Plot its growth and changes throughout the year. Measure the height and circumference of a fast growing tree regularly and make a graph.

2 Changes

Use a small twig from a tree and cut it so that it looks like the trunk and branches of a tree. Stick it to a piece of paper and using seasonal colours paint the leaf patterns of the tree around the twig (see photo). By using four similar twigs, it is possible to show the four seasons of change for a tree.

3 Leaf sorting

Collect lots of leaves of different shapes, sizes and colours. Sort them accordingly. Include words such as *round, serrated, pointed, irregular, red, yellow, russet, green* and make a display. Measure the length and width of the largest and smallest leaves. Find out which leaves come from which trees. Once the sorting is finished, the children can use the leaves together with acorns or berries to make up collage pictures for a frieze as in the illustration.

4 Autumn on the farm

Make a visit to a local farm and collect examples of common plants such as cereals, berries, fir cones and apples. Make drawings of the different plants and bake some bread. Encourage children to produce bread mice, a plat or other small bread creations. This activity can involve discussion of changes to materials as well as studying autumnal plants.

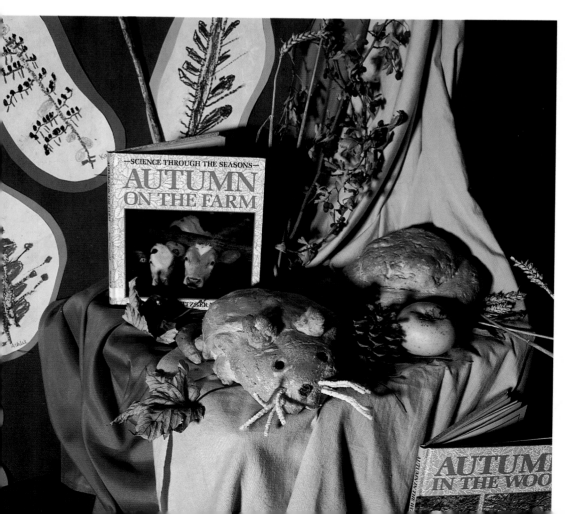

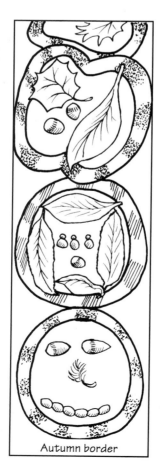

Autumn border

Further activities

1 Plant spotting

Take the children into the school grounds and ask them to find as many plants as possible. Encourage them to make drawings and produce a class poster of all of the plants, labelled and coloured.

2 Other living things ideas

See page 72 for creation stories. See pages 76-79 for Planet Phobos.

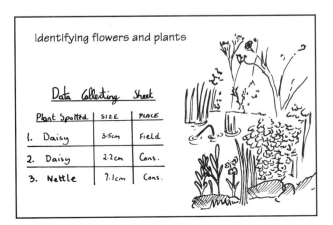

Identifying flowers and plants

Data Collecting Sheet

Plant Spotted	SIZE	PLACE
1. Daisy	3·5cm	Field
2. Daisy	2·2cm	Cons.
3. Nettle	7·1cm	Cons.

Try these investigations

Using a line transect: Take a piece of cord 5 metres long and stretch it across part of the school field or conservation area. On every 25 cm measured make a red mark, called a station. Identify the plant species found at that point and measure the height of it in centimetres. Record the data on a collection sheet and show the frequency and height of plants in the field using a bar graph with a key for the types of plants as shown in illustration. Work out the percentages of plants found on the line transect station points, (see above).

Identifying flowers and plants: Get each child to choose a flower in the conservation area or school field. Use reference books to find out what kind of flower they have found, drawing the flower on a piece of paper with a scale drawn alongside. Write up a definition of the flower such as: 'The yellow flag: it has three landing places, the three largest and most strikingly coloured petals. The smaller petals stand upright and take no part in pollination. The three yellow petals have a stigma lip which is sensitive to pollen.'

Living things - animals

First activities

1 Study of fish
Study the school aquarium and record the pattern and duration of feeding on Monday, Wednesday and Friday. Produce a colour coded clock to show feeding times.

2 Fish mobile
Look at Matisse's goldfish pictures. Make a mobile of goldfish (see photo) as part of an animal colouration and movement study.

3 Microscopic underwater life
Use books to talk about small underwater creatures and the role they play in food chains.

Further activities

1 Sea life display

Collect a wide variety of sea creatures, shells and fish. Try to supplement pictures with specimens from library or museum education services. Make a quiz, getting the children to find out what they are, label and put them into groups (crustacea, fish), and add to an underwater display such as the one in the photograph above.

2 Our fish book

Sometimes school pets die. As part of a life cycle study, such an event can be used to understand some of the processes of life. The illustration shows a book which contains the story of the life and death of one of the school's pet fish.

First activities

1 New life

As part of an Easter topic, get the children: to draw and paint flowers, to make up eggs using papier maché and balloons, and to make young creatures such as chicks, ducklings or even baby dinosaurs from papier maché which can then be painted. Talk about spring representing renewal and refer to creation stories.

Eggs made from papier maché

2 Infinite variety

Discuss stories of creation and how religions and myths account for the vast range of creatures found on earth. Make drawings of animals. Make a class book on creation stories. Include material from the next activity.

3 What creature is that?

Use a key to identify different creatures as shown in the illustration below.

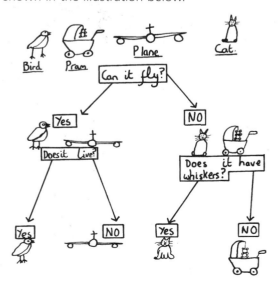

4 Noises animals make

What sounds do animals make? List the sounds suggested by your children such as squawks, roars, purrs, barks, hoots and growls. Which animals make these noises? Get children to make pictures of animals and to write out a label for the sound most likely to be associated with the animals. Make a frieze.

5 Who am I?

Make up some posters using mystery lines such as: *I have crinkly skin, I walk slowly, I carry my home, I am a ...* Make some very easy ones and a few that are more difficult. Put them on the wall. Discuss the statements with the children and ask them to identify each animal and then make drawings to go with it. Double mount the pictures and add the pictures to the display.

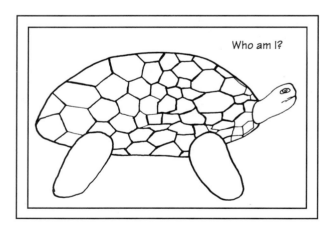

6 Natural colours

Talk about the colours found in nature such as in plants (red cabbage), in animals (octopus's ink, parrots, chameleons) etc. Discuss the use of these colours, e.g. for camouflage, warnings of danger, attracting mates, etc. Cut out some butterfly shapes from folded paper, daub bright colours on one side making a pattern, fold together, rub and open out to show a symmetrical pattern.

Further activities

1 Tadpole diary

Read the story *Tadpole diary* by David Drew (Rigby Education, 1987, ISBN 0454 014627) as a starting point for studying the frog life cycle. Use magnifying glasses to study frog spawn as it grows into full size frogs. Always take great care when handling animals. Use clay to make little frogs and paint them green. Dark red kidney beans can be used for the tadpoles (put them on a white paper plate and draw their tails). The eggs can be black dots in the middle of each bubble on a plastic bubble wrap. When the study of the cycle has been completed, children can make a class big tadpole diary to include drawings, poems and writing on the growth stages.

2 Frog odyssey

Make a class book on how frogs manage to survive even when they have to move their home.

Try this investigation

Pond creatures: Get the children (under careful supervision) to use a net to dip into the pond at different depths: 10 cms, 30 cms, 50 cms and so on. Count and identify the creatures found at these depths. Make symbols for the different creatures and plot these on a graph to show the frequency of species at different depths. Draw conclusions.

3 Identifying pond creatures

Provide pond nets, pencils, rulers, graph paper and transparent containers. Ask the children to dip carefully into the pond until they find something interesting. Place specimens into the water filled container. Place the graph paper under the container so that the creatures can be measured and the measurements marked on the graph paper. Multiply the millimetres by ten and get the children to make a large drawing of the creatures. Use pond books to help identify the specimens. The children may be surprised to find that some 'beetles' turn out to be dragonfly larvae.

4 Pond charter

Talk about how we must look after our environment and should be careful when studying all living creatures. Make a class behaviour charter, decorate and display it. Include statements such as: *Don't leave litter. Take care when examining creatures.*

First activities

1 It's a small world

Ask children to bring in their smallest favourite toys such as houses, animals, soldiers, beads or tiny pencils. Display them and talk about how there are other small worlds inhabited by minibeasts. Ask questions such as: Where can minibeasts be found? What do they look like? The photograph shows a simple collage of a split tree trunk where lots of minibeasts have their secret homes. A working display like this can change as the topic progresses.

2 Minibeast Quiz

Make a wall display of twelve different un-named but numbered minibeasts. Include some facts written around them such as: 'Three out of every four animals in the world are minibeasts. Mini means small. Minibeasts are small creatures such as snails, woodlice, spiders and ants. Many minibeasts are insects which have a miraculous way of changing their shape up to four times in their life. Minibeasts are invertebrates; unlike birds, fish and mammals they have no backbone. There are minibeasts that can live on land, in water and in the air. Wherever you live there will be minibeasts!'

Name: Stephenie Robson

MINI-BEAST QUIZ

I think that the minibeasts are:

1. Water slater
2. Dyticus beetle
3. Water boatman
4. Grasshopper
5. Peacock caterpillar
6. Spider
7. Bee
8. Ant
9. Wood louse
10. Snail
11. Centipede
12. Devil's coach-horse

minibeasts? where?

Further activities

1 Creatures from the soil

This can be a topic activity expanding into all subject areas of the curriculum. Ask children questions such as: What is soil made of? How many types of soil can we find? How can we describe soil? How much water does soil hold? What lives in the soil? How can soil be sorted? Then talk about the creatures who live in the soil and ask questions about where they live and how, how they grow and what they eat, how they move. Talk about minibeasts and how we can identify them. Are they all pests? How can we control pests? Do all spiders and ants behave in the same way? Can children create a suitable environment for minibeasts to live in? Talk about the clues we need to look for in order to find some minibeasts.

2 Invent a bug

Based on their knowledge of insects, children are asked to imagine and design a 'mega-beast'. They give their insects a name and describe them including: how they move, what they eat, where they live, whether they are dangerous and to whom, etc.

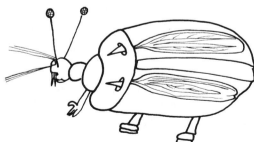

Super Bloodsucking laser beetle

It can...
See in the dark, fly,
fire defensive spikes at predators,
kill leeches with fangs,
Pick up radio waves with its
antenae and climb up a vertical
rockface unhurt.

It eats leeches and greenfly.

Can you find out what type of spiders these are?

3 Spider in the class

Discuss with the children which is the most likely minibeast to live in your class and look around carefully for some clues (little holes around the corners, spider's web, soil on the floor, etc). Concentrate on spiders and their varieties. Make a huge black spider with red eyes out of papier maché and hang it securely on a ceiling sized web made from rope and string. Find some toy flies and spiders and place them on the web. Children can draw different kinds of spiders with the help of books, and then make a quiz for the whole class to identify them.

4 School grounds expedition

Measure the school grounds and make a wall map. Colour code the different areas of grounds according to the soil found there (dry, wet, stones, vegetation, etc). Divide the children into groups and allocate an area to search for mini creatures. Children make drawings of what they found and bring some soil in small sample bags. Exhibit pictures of their findings with the soil sample and explanations of why the animals found lived there.

First activities

1 Owl

Cut out a large black shape to represent branches of a tree and place it on a blue background. Talk to the children about how owls look, sound and live. Ask children to make their own owl collages using a variety of scrap materials. Arrange these on the branches with some labels similar to those on the photograph.

2 Animal feet

Talk about how animals move. Have a look at the children's feet, discuss with them and ask what they can say about their feet. Make a note of their observations. Set the task of finding five animals which have different feet. Make drawings and use as part of class book or display. Ask questions about the different forms of feet. What is the purpose of a duck's webbed feet (link environment with the physical form of feet)? Extend this to search for different types of coats, soft ones, rough ones, furry and downy ones.

3 Caring for your pets

Discuss pet animals, what they need to keep healthy and how we should care for them. Ask the children to draw their favourite pet, writing on one side of the drawing what their pet needs (food, water, love, care, warmth, exercise etc).

4 *The very hungry caterpillar*

Read the book and talk about caterpillars. Get the children to make drawings of the foods the caterpillar ate and include these in a display as shown in the illustration.

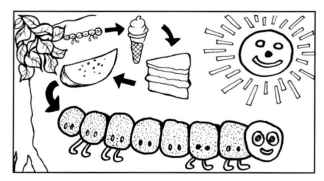

5 Ladybirds

Get the children to make simple ladybirds (circles of coloured paper with black paint for spots and red pieces of tissue paper stuck on) and some butterflies as shown below. Make a display positioning all the butterflies on one side and the ladybirds on the other.

Fold, cut   *Add paint fold in*   *Open out*

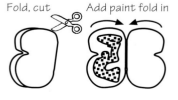

Further activities

1 Animals in mythology

Collect pictures of strange and mythical creatures. Discuss how visual information about animals was collected before photography. Talk about scientific drawings and the need for accuracy, detail and scale.

2 Observational drawings

Use photographs of badgers or some other creature, or if possible borrow a specimen from your museum service. Get the children to study this carefully and make detailed drawings.

Try this investigation

Guided observation: Take the children into the school conservation area and search for creatures (use some magnifiers). Ask a set of questions such as: Can you see its eyes? When back in class ask the children to describe in writing and drawings what they saw.

More animal ideas: Explore how animals have featured in mythology and religion. Talk about how reports of animals in history were often misrepresented. Talk about endangered species. Link with Activities on pages 77-78 (Life cycles of animals and plants on the planet Phobos).

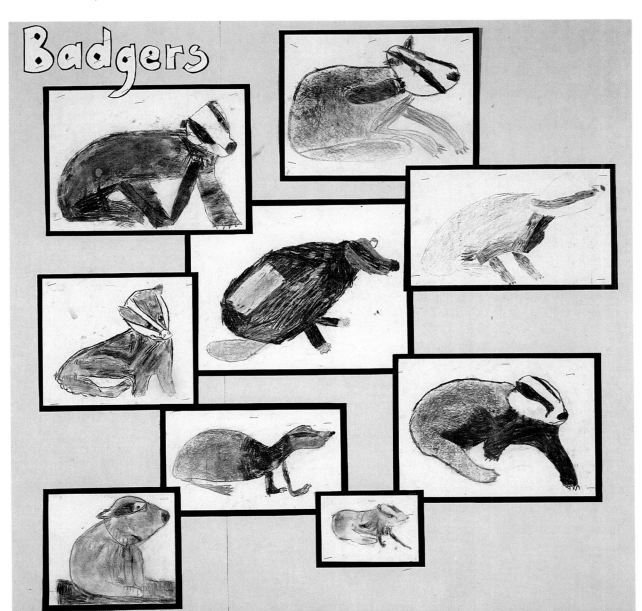

Badgers

Living things -

Try this investigation

Environment detectives: A visit to a nature reserve or large park can develop into a complete environmental research project. The interrelation of humans, other animals, plants and the seasonal changes can be studied. The photographs show different aspects of such a visit to Lydiard Park. Equipment required for such a visit may include nets, jam jars, data recording sheets, coloured pencils and pens, cameras and films. The investigation is described in the following activities.

1 Collecting data

Use a data recording sheet to collect information by looking at evidence of life around you and answering questions such as: Has it got a shell? Has it got wings? How many legs has it got? Other methods of recording data can include photographs and drawings.

2 Nature poems

Set aside a quiet time in the park for the children to use their senses and to make notes of what they can see, hear, smell, touch and feel. They can make drawings and write words and sentences to be used to make poems and paintings back in class. As an extension to this the children can use wax crayons (the metallic colours are good for this) to make a rubbings record of their visit. The rubbings can be mounted as part of a finished display about the visit.

investigating environments

3 A survey

Prepare a survey sheet as shown in the photograph. Encourage the children to look for signs of the impact of human beings on a particular environment. The survey results can be collated and used to produce bar graphs of frequency against a number of variables.

4 Adapting to the environment

Extend the investigation and look at plant, animal and human homes. Search for evidence of food chains in the countryside (or the park). Talk about ways that living things have adapted to their environments and discuss the need for environmental protection.

Learning objectives

- Different plants and animals are found in different habitats.
- Keys can help identify living things in their local environments.
- Plants and animals are suited to their environments.
- Plants and animals depend on each other.
- Food chains show feeding relationships between living things.
- All food chains start with plants, not necessarily green plants.
- Living things have to compete and adapt to survive in an environment.

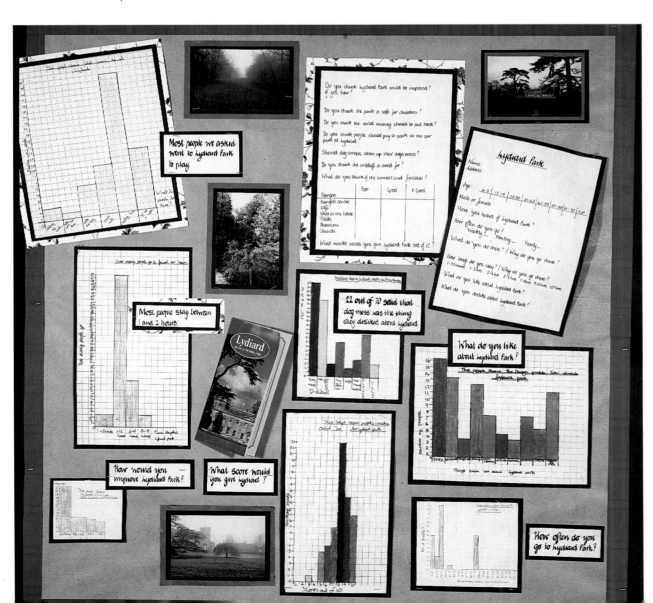

water

First activities

1 Waterproofing

Talk about how important it is to be warm and dry in bad weather and ask about what kind of clothes children wear when it is wet. Look at some of their raincoats. Some will be plastic and some of cotton that has been treated. Collect scrap materials such as wool, cotton, plastic, paper and nylon and ask the children which of these will make the best raincoat for a soft toy. Test them by placing samples of the materials over a jam jar and pour water on to the surface.

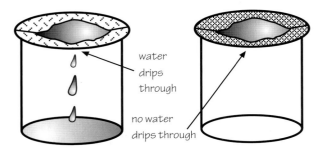

water drips through

no water drips through

Further activities

1 Filtering mud

Stress the importance of clean water to good health and ask the children to design a system for filtering muddy water. Use a filter funnel, filter paper, sand, fine gravel and beakers. Make some water muddy and filter it as in the photograph and illustration.

2 The water cycle

Discuss with the children how water is heated, evaporates and condenses again to produce rain. Demonstrate this as shown in the illustration. Get the children to do their own detailed diagram of the water cycle as in the photograph - opposite and the illustration on page 49.

3 Water poems and shaped drawings

Make some symmetrical drawings of seagulls and cut them so that they are framed in triangular shapes or in the shape of water drops. Mount on blue background. Play a recording of *La mer* (Debussy) or sound effects of the sea and get the children to write poems about water.

Learning objectives

- Different materials can look, smell and feel similar or different.
- Materials can be sorted into groups according to texture, appearance or smell.
- Materials can be sorted into groups according to buoyancy.
- Materials can be sorted into groups according to whether they are magnetic or not.
- Materials can be sorted into made and natural groups.
- Many everyday things are made from common materials.
- Certain materials can be used in lots of ways.
- Certain materials are best for specific uses on the basis of their properties.

2 Water collage

Collect together scrap materials and get the children to make their own water collages as in the photograph on the opposite page.

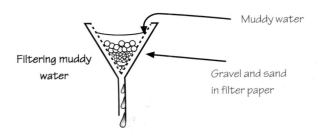

Muddy water

Filtering muddy water

Gravel and sand in filter paper

Try this investigation

Dissolving: Use a range of materials, some which dissolve and some which do not dissolve, such as brown sugar, bath crystals, sand, coffee powder and talcum powder. Ask the children to predict which ones will dissolve in water and then use equal amounts of each material and stir them into equal amounts of water for the same amount of time. See what will happen and use simple tables to record the results.

Floating or sinking: Collect together objects such as small plastic and metal toys, a piece of wood, a tennis ball, a felt-tip pen, a fir cone and a metal screw. Ask children to predict which items will float and which will sink. Conduct a fair test using a bowl of water and record the results.

41

Materials –

Introduction

Materials can be grouped according to simple qualities: metals may be magnetic or not, everday materials can be made or natural, hard or soft. A story such as *The Iron Man* is ideal for starting all kinds of activities about materials for both young and older children. These two pages show how the idea can be used for children of different ages.

First activities

1 Collecting and sorting

Collect a group of objects and ask the children to group them and say how they are similar. Encourage them to use their senses of sight, smell and touch to sort them in different ways. Use the materials as part of an 'iron man' display. Include questions such as: Are these all metal? How many different ways can you sort the metals? Are any of the metals magnetic?

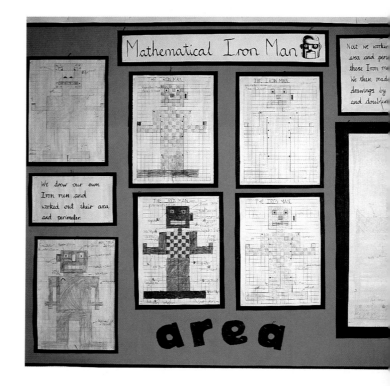

2 Mathematical Man

Use squared paper to make designs which can be counted square by square to calculate the area of the Iron Man and the perimeter.

3 From description to model

Use the book and get the children to write their own descriptions of the Iron Man. From these descriptions get the children to make a model or a detailed drawing.

The Iron Man

Further activities

1 Electrical Iron Man
Design a simple circuit using batteries, bulbs and switches to make the Iron Man's eyes light up

2 Natural or made?
After discussion give children cards with descriptive words on and go on a treasure hunt around the school looking for natural and made materials. Use a worksheet to record the findings of the hunt.

3 Still life quiz
Collect a variety of products. Include a bicycle, toaster, toys and other interesting items. Arrange the display to include labels with the materials' names on them. Name all the raw materials that have been used to make the exhibits. Place the labels randomly. Get the children to sort the names, placing them alongside the appropriate materials.

4 Computer Iron Man
Use a computer program such as Artisan to illustrate episodes from the story.

5 Iron man's heaven - magnetic or not?
Get the children to bring in a range of materials for the 'Iron Man's heaven' as in the photograph. Try to include safety pins, aluminium foil and plastic materials (you will need a big horse shoe magnet). Ask them to predict which materials are magnetic and which ones are not. Use worksheets to predict, test, record and draw conclusions about magnetic qualities of materials.

Materials -

Introduction

Any one type of material can be investigated in many ways. Paper can be durable, waterproof, good for drawing on and for making aeroplanes with. You will need eight types of paper such as photocopy paper, coloured art paper, metal finished paper, hand made paper and blotting paper, to be used in each of the investigations. Children can fair test to find out which kind of paper is suitable for the different purposes.

Activities

1 Best for waterproofing

Cut squares from a number of types of paper. Fold them as shown in the illustration. Open them out and place them on top of clear plastic containers. Pour measured amounts of water onto the centre of each piece of folded paper, leave for an hour and measure the amount of water that has dripped through the paper. This activity can be extended by improving the waterproofing of paper by applying wax or oil to its surface and retesting.

2 Best for absorbing water

Place equal sized pieces of paper onto the surface of a bowl of water. Leave for one minute and then wring out all the water into a container. Compare the amounts soaked up by each sample and record the results.

3 Best for painting on

In class discussion, agree on the qualities needed for a painting paper. Should the paper allow water to flow and soak in, merging softly with neighbouring colours or should it dry quickly allowing colours to remain clean and separate from each other? Prepare a data collection sheet with these criteria and test a range of papers.

4 Strongest when wet

Get the children to devise a fair test to find out which kind of paper is strongest when wet.

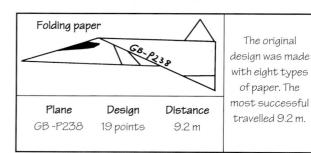

Folding paper

GB-P238

Plane	Design	Distance
GB -P238	19 points	9.2 m

The original design was made with eight types of paper. The most successful travelled 9.2 m.

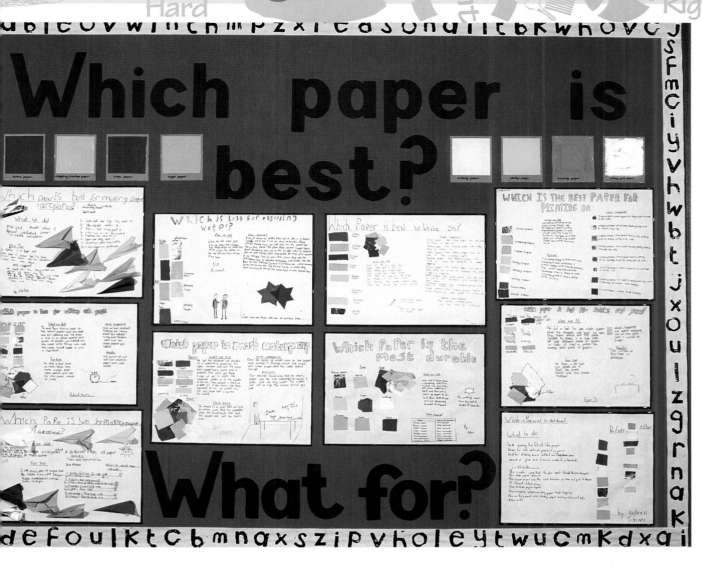

5 Fair testing paper aeroplanes

Allow the children to choose eight types of paper to construct paper aeroplanes. Ask them to consider how to make their tests fair. They may decide that it is important that each piece of paper is the same size and shape and that the model designs should be the same. If you are testing the models outside, children may want to make sure there is no wind.

6 Easy to stick

Get the children to test which papers are the easiest to stick to a background paper using a water based glue.

7 Best to write on

Give the children eight samples of different paper and ask them to find out which is the best to write on using a fountain pen. In their conclusions they should use the word 'because'.

8 Best for durability

Provide eight samples of the same kinds of paper as in the previous activity. Can the children devise a test for durability? They may simply count the number of times an eraser can be rubbed over the paper surface before it forms a hole.

First activities

1 Comparing materials

Collect a variety of objects that have obviously different characteristics. Include a soft plastic bottle, a feather, a transparent ruler, a cardboard box, a safety mirror, a knobbly branch, a smooth piece of wood. Write some words on flash cards that describe the qualities of the objects, such as *transparent, flexible, hard,* and *shiny*. Mix the objects and labels randomly on the table and get the children to sort them.

2 Bouncing

Make a collection of different balls. Ask the children to say which one they think will bounce the highest. Try them out and see whether the results are as expected.

3 Feely Quiz

Place some known materials into feely boxes and let the children touch and describe them. Place some different materials in the feely boxes and ask the children if they can identify them and make drawings. Make a touch display including the objects and drawings.

4 What am I?

Allow the children to choose objects with textured surfaces and ask them to write a description of them ending with the question: What am I? Make a drawing and mount the work on a background of tissue paper and reflective foils as in the photograph above.

Suitable materials

Further activities

1 Homes

Bring in examples of modern building materials and get the children to sort them into natural and made materials. Find out what kind of building materials are used locally and ask children to make rubbings. Use a map of your area and with map pins mark where the children live. Get the children to draw the front of their house and to consider how buildings and homes have changed over time. Extend the activity by asking: What would cavemen use to build a shelter? Ask children to design and make their own cavemen's homes using clay and various fabrics (see photo).

Try this investigation

Separating mixtures of materials: Give the children mixtures of sand and salt, salt and iron filings, salt and water and sand and water. Provide equipment such as beakers, a filter funnel, filter papers and a magnet. Challenge the children to separate the mixtures. The dry of sand and salt can be separated by dissolving the salt in water, filtering off and drying the sand on the filter paper whilst the water is evaporated leaving the salt. Iron filings can be removed from the salt by using a magnet (cover the magnet with paper first to make it easier to clean and to collect iron filings).

Cover magnet with paper before trying to separate materials

Separating mixtures

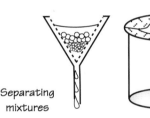

Mixtures of sand and salt can be separated by filtering

Solids can be removed from water by evaporation

Material changes -

First activities

1 Which liquid is the runniest?

Start this activity by posing a few simple questions: Which liquid is the runniest? Is it water? Washing up liquid? Treacle? Or oil ? Work with the children to devise an experiment to find out.

2 Changing shape

Give the children some Plasticine or dough that can be formed into different shapes. Measure the amounts given out so that they are the same. Ask the children to use all of the material and make unusual shapes or long thin/fat short animals. Reinforce that it is the same amount of material in each even though the shapes are different.

3 Ice melts

Get children to describe what they observe as they watch ice (or snow) melting. Ask a helper to write down the children's comments.

4 Cooking

Have a practical cookery session and make cakes or Easter biscuits. Talk about how some changes are permanent whilst others can be reversed.

5 Fiery dragon

Use a variety of materials, some shiny paper, some cut paper and some patterned paper changed by applying dripped paint, to make a fantastic creature as in the illustration.

Further activities

1 Making dyes from natural materials

Collect onion skins, pieces of red cabbage and lichen. Boil these separately with pieces of fabric, making a note of the colour of the fabric before and after the process. Are the colours fast or can they be washed out? Try adding salt to the mixture and see if it makes any difference.

2 Leaf prints

Have a variety of fresh leaves. Keep them in a plastic bag as they do not print well if they are dried out too much. You will need plenty of newspaper and three or four colours - these will allow your children to mix a wide range of colours themselves. Place a leaf on a bed of newspaper, paint it carefully, turn it over onto a clean piece of paper, smoothly rub down. Remove the leaf to reveal the print. Continue until an interesting arrangement of prints has been achieved. This activity can be undertaken using dyes and fabric. After the prints have dried the children can examine closely the structure of the leaves using a magnifying glass.

reversible & irreversible

3 Dyeing

Collect a range of white natural and made fabrics, including cotton, silk, wool, nylon and other made fabrics. Cut small samples (approx. 15cm square). Sort the samples using agreed categories such as: made, natural, soft, rough or simply by colour.

Discuss with the children the various differences that there may be between the samples. For examples Nylon may be made from mono or multi filament strands and some fabrics may be composed of smoother threads than others. Ask questions about how these characteristics could affect the way the fabrics accept dyes. Get the children to use microscopes and make detailed drawings of the fabrics. Use Dylon or similar cold water dyes and test the fabrics. Which ones accept and retain the dyes the best? Record and present the drawings, dyed samples and observations as a display.

Learning objectives

- The shape of some materials can be changed by simple physical processes.
- The mass of an object is not changed by simple physical processes.
- Some everyday materials can change state by heating and cooling.
- Some changes in materials are reversible and some are irreversible.

5 Eggs

Study some raw eggs making detailed drawings and notes (children using pastels on dark paper often find it easier to make accurate drawings). Boil one egg for two minutes and another for seven minutes. Cut these in half and get the children to make further careful drawings and notes. Ask the children if they think that cooking an egg can be reversed or not.

4 Evaporation

Talk about the different states of materials, gasses, liquids and solids. Make a drawing of the particles in each of these. Cover a bowl of water with a polythene bag and seal it. Place in direct sunlight and ask the children to observe and record what happened. Get the children to make diagrams of the water cycle as shown below.

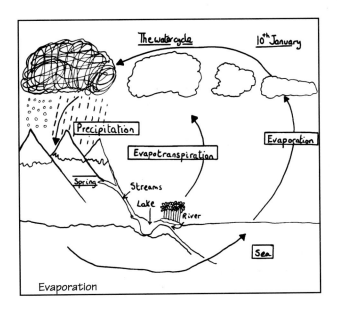

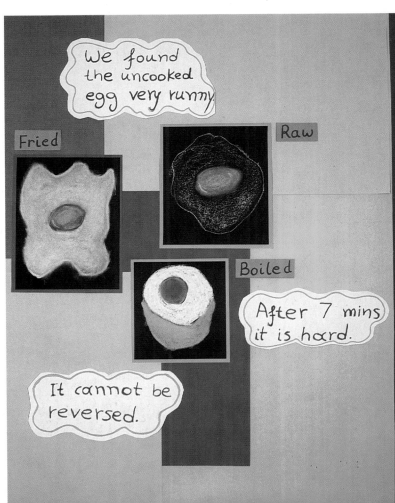

Material changes -

First activities

1 Making models

Offer a variety of materials to the children with which they can make models of brothers, sisters, mothers and fathers. Arrange the models as a small display. Discuss with the children what materials have been used, write them on card and include in the display as shown.

2 Mass and shape

Demonstrate how a measured amount of Plasticine can be stretched, squeezed or pulled and yet it remains the same mass. The Plasticine can be weighed using conkers or normal weights, or alternatively can be forced back into its original container. After demonstrating, get the children to work in pairs to investigate the idea further by making large flat shapes, squat animal models and snakes. In each case all of the Plasticine should be used and the finished models should be weighed to see if the mass has changed.

3 Book week marbled poster

Introduce marbling by half filling a bottle with coloured oil and topping up with water. Demonstrate how the two liquids are immiscible by turning the stoppered bottle upside down. For marbling use NES Arnold marbling inks carefully dropped, drop by drop, onto a tray of water. Try some metallic inks as well as normal colours. Gently move the surface of the water to achieve an interesting effect. Place white or coloured paper onto the water surface then lift carefully from one corner. Allow to dry. The marbled paper can be used for a poster as in the photograph. Marbling can also be used as a way of introducing creative writing, as the images are often most evocative of strange places or dreams.

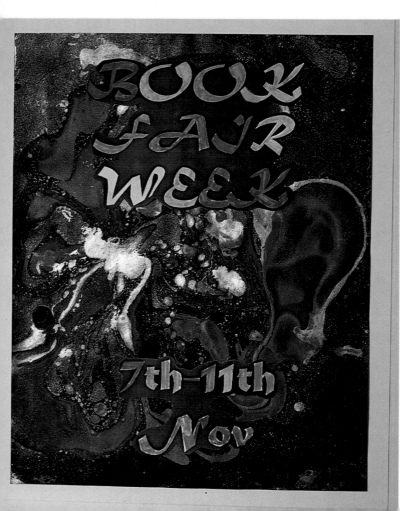

Colour, cut out and stick letters to marbled paper to make poster

Computer generated letters

using materials

Further activities

1 Collage environmental plan

Using patterns, colours or signs to represent other things is common in scientific notation and diagrams. The photograph shows how a survey of the environs of one school has been transformed into a lively wall hanging using a variety of textured materials. Ensure that the backing is a strong support.

2 Paper making

Use a commercially produced paper making kit or prepare your own pulp from waste paper and fibres to make paper.

3 Plaster casts

Press children's hands into soft clay to make a perfect impression. Build a wall around the clay as shown. Mix plaster. Pour plaster into the clay moulds. Get the children to observe that as the plaster sets it gives off heat (it is *exothermic*), by gently placing hands on the setting plaster.

Hand impression in soft clay

Pour plaster into card surround

First activities

1 Blues

Get the children to use a variety of materials all of which are blue. Use them to make simple cut out balloons to be mounted on a blue background (as in the photograph) or as part of a submarine world. You can make a series of colour displays each focusing on one colour at a time. In a similar way pictures using one colour, such as blue, can effectively express a feeling such as those in the 'Cold 1997' pictures below.

2 Cool colours

Discuss with the children the names of a variety of colours and how they perceive them. Are they cool, warm, calm, exciting? When they are placed together do the combinations of colours appear to the children to be more exciting or more calming? Make a class frieze of colours that calm, and run through to those that are clashing.

3 Tie and dye

Use some old pieces of cotton and tie them roughly with string. Wet parts of the fabric and then place in a bath of cold water dye such as Dylon or some dyes you can make up from natural materials (see page 49 Activity 2).

4 Paired investigation

Give pairs of children two labels such as *brittle* and *tough*. Ask them to find and sort examples of materials that are brittle and tough. Other pairs can look for shiny/dull materials, materials that smell good/bad or materials that can float or sink.

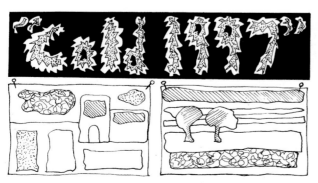

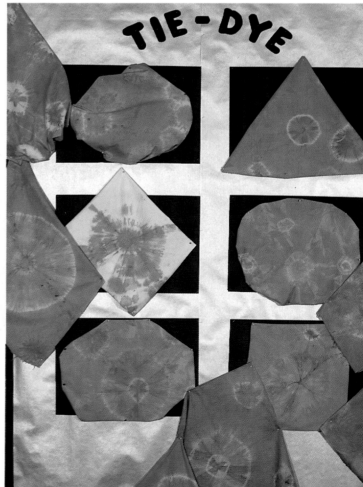

Further activities

1 Recycled art

Discuss the environmental problems that may be alleviated by recycling materials. Discuss how artists such as Picasso and Braque used *Found Objects* and materials (often just rubbish!) to create collages, sculptures and as subjects for their Cubist compositions. The photograph, above, shows the work of a group of children interpreting a cubist picture. To extend work on recycling, get the children to design logos for products that contain materials that can be recycled.

Try this investigation

Strong bags: Collect six different plastic and paper carrier bags. Ask the children to examine the bags and predict what weight they can carry. Will the bag be strong enough to support 15Kg? Will the handle break or will the bottom tear? Record the predictions. Then use weights to load the bags progressively (1Kg at a time), until 15Kg is reached or the bag breaks (whichever is first). For those bags that do break observe where and at what load they break. Record the results and present with the predictions and conclusions. Can children identify the strongest materials for making bags?

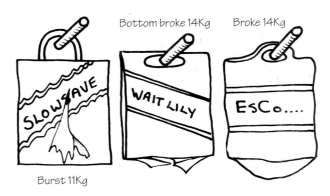

Took 15Kg — FAINSBURY

Handle broke 7Kg — Bo-op

Bottom broke 10Kg — DOORWAY

Burst 11Kg — SLOWSAVE

Bottom broke 14Kg — WAIT LILY

Broke 14Kg — EsCo....

Activities

1 George's Marvellous Medicine

This story is a great way of giving a new perspective on changes in materials. Read the story, make a display (such as shown in the photograph) and ask the children to explain how and why Granny changed.

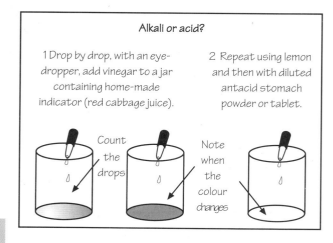

Alkali or acid?

1 Drop by drop, with an eye-dropper, add vinegar to a jar containing home-made indicator (red cabbage juice).

2 Repeat using lemon and then with diluted antacid stomach powder or tablet.

Count the drops

Note when the colour changes

Try this investigation

Testing for changes: You will need lemon, vinegar, water and solutions of antacid stomach tablets or powder (made by mixing with equal quantities of water) for this experiment. Even though these chemicals are not dangerous you can explain to the children the need to take care with handling chemicals. Testing for acids and alkalines is a basic chemical procedure. You can make your own testing solution: boil some red cabbage leaves and stir them until the water is strongly coloured. Place small amounts of cabbage water in three clear plastic pots. Drop by drop add vinegar to the first pot. How many drops does it take for the cabbage water to change colour? Drop lemon juice into the second pot and a dilute solution of antacid into the third. Acids will tend to change the cabbage water into red whilst alkalis will turn it green. Use cabbage water to test the acidity of soil, toothpaste, cola and other common substances.

Material changes

Further activities

1 Tooth decay

Make a simple class survey of how many children have cavities. Ask the children why they think teeth decay: Is it normal? Is it inevitable? Is there something in food that causes it? Contact your local dental hospital (or dentist) and get four human teeth. Place one tooth in a glass of water that has been boiled, place another in a similar quantity of a branded cola, the third in milk and the fourth in a squeezed lemon. Get the children to make annotated drawings of the teeth and to observe what happens over a period of two weeks. Ask them to explain what happened.

2 Illustrated tooth poem

Read the children, 'Oh, I wish I'd looked after me Teeth' by Pam Ayres (see *I like this poem*, K. Webb (ed.) Puffin) and get them to make up their own illustrated version as below.

Try this investigation

The great burying test: Collect photographs and bring in some objects that show decay e.g. rusting cars, fresh and rotting leaves, worn out shoes and clothes, fresh and rotting food (fruit and bread). Discuss with the children the reasons for decay and conduct an experiment to find out why iron rusts and how long fruit takes to rot. Select four or five different types of materials including an apple, plastic toys, a tin can, a stainless steel spoon and an old shoe. Bury these in the ground and conduct a great burying test (as in the photograph) by examining the items after four weeks and recording the differences found.

3 Test for buoyancy

Take two sample materials e.g. Plasticine and balsa wood. Discuss how they are similar and different. Give the children pairs of everyday materials (cork, stone, jam jar lid, wooden spatula, bath sponge, toothbrush, plastic toy car etc.) and ask them questions such as: Do they float? Can you make them float?

Oh, I wish I'd looked after my teeth,
And spotted the perils beneath,
All the toffees I chewed,
And the sweet sticky food,
Oh, I wish I'd looked after my teeth.

FRIEND
My mother she told me no end,
'If you've got a tooth, you got a friend'
I was young then, and careless,
My toothbrush was hairless,
I never had much time to spend.

How I laughed at my mothers false teeth,
As they foamed in the waters beneath,
But now comes the reckonin'
It's me they are beckonin'
Oh, I wish I'd looked after my teeth!

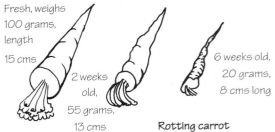

Fresh, weighs 100 grams, length 15 cms

2 weeks old, 55 grams, 13 cms

6 weeks old, 20 grams, 8 cms long

Rotting carrot

55

Material changes -

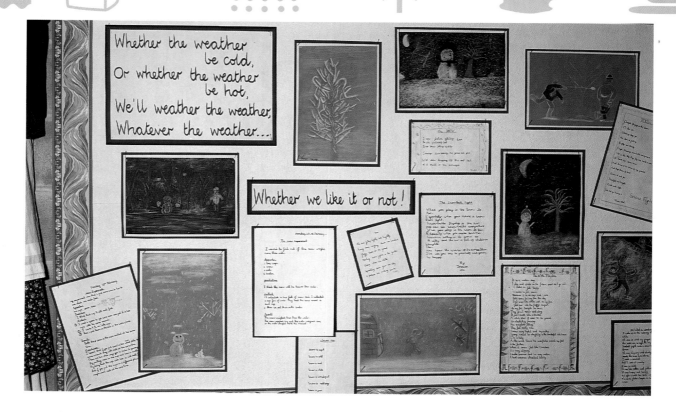

Introduction

Weather and seasons are often used as starting points for creative work. They can also start scientific investigations about changes to materials. During a snowy period, introduce ideas about how materials can change by reading the children *Winter morning* by Ogden Nash:

> Winter is the king of showmen,
> Turning tree stumps into snow men
> And houses into birthday cakes
> And spreading sugar over the lakes.
> Smooth and clean and frost white
> The world looks good enough to bite.
> That's the season to be young,
> Catching snowflakes on your tongue.
>
> Snow is snowy when it's snowing
> I'm sorry it's slushy when it's going.

Activities

1 Snow pictures and poems

Get the children to observe snow falling and settling. Make notes and sketches which can then be used as the basis of poems or paintings.

2 Snowy day class book

Take some photographs of the effects of snow on the local environment and animals. Collect experiments, photographs, drawings and poems and combine these with in a class book.

Try this investigation

Snow and water: Does snow weigh the same as water? A simple investigation can be undertaken as part of a mini-project on winter. Fill a cup to the brim with snow, weigh it. Note the weight and reweigh the cup once the snow has melted. Record the results and draw conclusions. (If there is no snow, use two or three ice cubes instead).

Whether the weather be hot: Does snow always melt at the same speed? The investigation here is to see if two identical cups of snow will melt at the same rate if they are placed side by side on a windowsill. Ask the children to complete the experiment and then suggest ways of changing one variable that would cause the two cups of snow to melt after different times.

3 Any old boots

Try to borrow examples of early clothing from a museum education service and supplement these with contemporary pieces and old shoes or boots. Get the children to examine the garments, find out what they are made of (natural or made materials) and estimate (from the materials used) how old they are.

4 Material landscapes

Give children A4 white cartridge paper. Get them to paint bright bands of colour horizontally, then to paint a contrasting dark area with three or four fine dark lines for tree trunks. Stick dried fern fronds, berries and leaves to complete the landscapes as in the photograph. Make a decorative frame as shown.

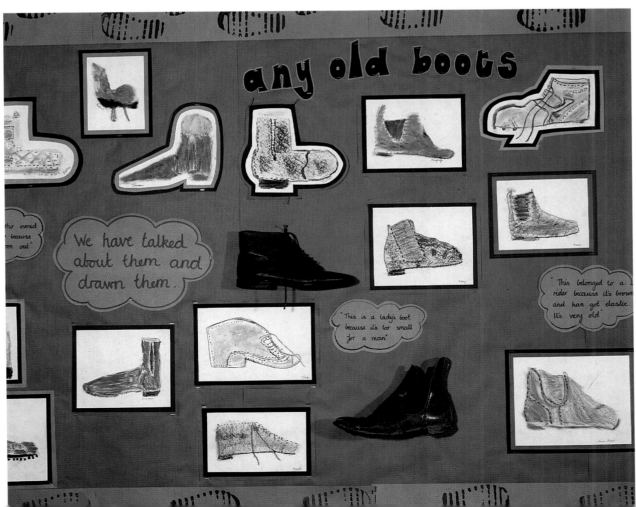

First activities

1 Water play

Playing with water, sand, pushing and pulling toys (small ones on strings and large ones with children on them) will help children to identify the physical forces of pushing and pulling. Make a visit to a water mill. Discuss how the wheel and the mechanisms are driven by the power of water. Can the children identify pushes and pulls to be found in a water mill? Make simple diagrams with arrows to show the direction of forces.

2 Air pushes

Have a class discussion and make a display of things that can be moved by air or produce movement in air, such as a hairdryer (teacher operated!), sail boats, umbrellas, balloons, kites and windmills. Include some other things in the display and get the children to name the ones that are air powered.

Learning objectives

- The body can push and pull.
- Pushes and pulls can start things moving.
- Air and water can both push things.
- Pushing and pulling are different.
- Increasing force speeds things up.
- Decreasing force can slow things down.
- Sideways pushes or pulls make things swerve.
- Pushing and pulling can change the shape of objects.
- Gravity and magnets exert forces.

3 Water powered models

Get the children to design and make their own simple models that are powered by water. See if they can use water to speed up or slow down movements or perhaps design a more fantastic one that can light up the eyes of a robot by completing circuits as in the drawing below.

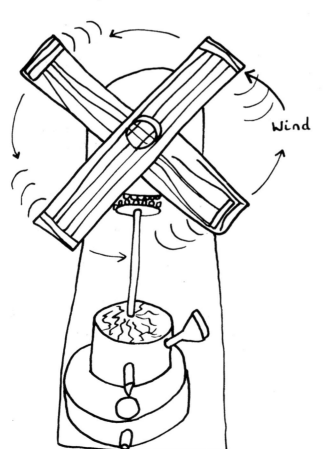

Wind

Try this investigation

Easier: Get the children to work in pairs pushing and pulling a range of objects that have the same mass, some with and some without wheels. Find out which are the easiest to move. Is it better to push or pull?

forces and motion

4 Swerving kicks

Have a practical session of football showing that a sideways kick pushes or pulls the football to make it swerve. Get the children to observe and explain swerving.

5 Changing shapes

Lead observation and investigations by pushing soft balloons, pulling elastic bands, stretching and squeezing clay, kneading and forming bread from dough. Explain that forces can change the shape of objects and get the children to record, by drawing, the effect of forces on soft objects.

Changing shapes

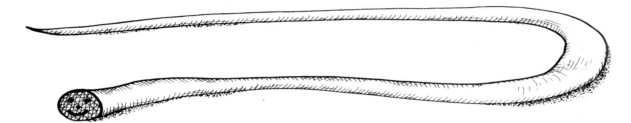

6 Forces in PE

During a PE session, work with a small group of children noting down the activities, movements and directions that children take. Back in class get the children to make small models of themselves doing activities from the PE lesson from thin card, glue and paint. Label the forces at work and make up a small display.

59

Falling

Do all things fall at the same speed?

How many ways can the children find to start a car rolling? How many ways of stopping a van moving?

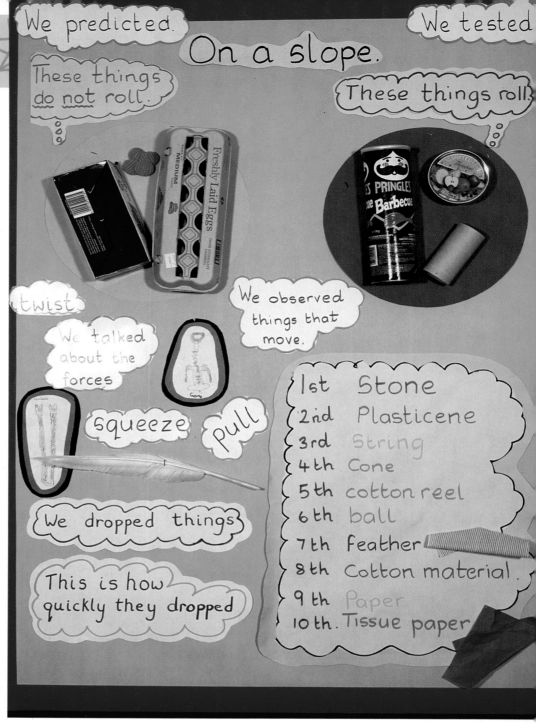

First activities

1 Things that roll

Make a collection of everyday objects such as egg cartons, cardboard rolls and small cartons (as in the photograph). Ask the children to predict which ones will roll down a slope and which ones will not. Test them and sort the results using a simple Venn diagram.

2 Dropping things

Make a collection of everyday materials including a feather, Plasticine, tissue paper as in the photograph. Drop each item from the same height and record the time they take to reach the floor. Explore with the children reasons for the results.

3 Pushing and pulling

Cut out pictures from magazines, include footballs being kicked, swimmers pushing the end of a pool, people pushing and pulling things such as door bells and shopping trolleys, and other physical actions that involve pushing and pulling. Make two labels, *Pushing* and *Pulling* and get the children to sort the pictures into two groups.

forces and motion

Further activities

1 Push and pull lists
Get the children to make a list of all the pushing and pulling activities they can think of. Choose two pulls and two pushes and make annotated drawings showing where forces are acting by using arrows.

2 Forces word bank
Ask the children to write down all the words they think relate to forces such as: *upthrust, friction, gravity, magnetism, push,* and *pull.* Include these in a wallet mounted on the wall or in a children's science book.

3 Finding the strongest magnet
Demonstrate one way of finding out which magnet of a group of different sized magnets is the strongest. On a smooth surface place two or three pins or paper clips. Alongside place a metre measure so that distances are easy to calculate. Place the first magnet to be tested a metre away from the pins, gradually bringing it closer until the pins are attracted to the magnet. Measure the distance and repeat this for the other magnets. Can the children find another way of testing magnets?

Try this investigation

Bouncing high: *Make a collection of different types of balls such as: ping pong, rubber, tennis, sponge rubber and a super bouncy ball. Get the children to predict how high each ball will bounce if dropped from a metre high. It is important to encourage the children to consider how to conduct a fair test, for example the illustration shows that the bottom of the ball should be consistently used as a measuring point. This activity can be extended by trying different surfaces upon which to drop the balls. Record the results.*

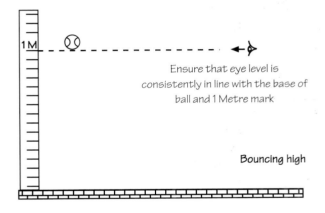

Ensure that eye level is consistently in line with the base of ball and 1 Metre mark

Bouncing high

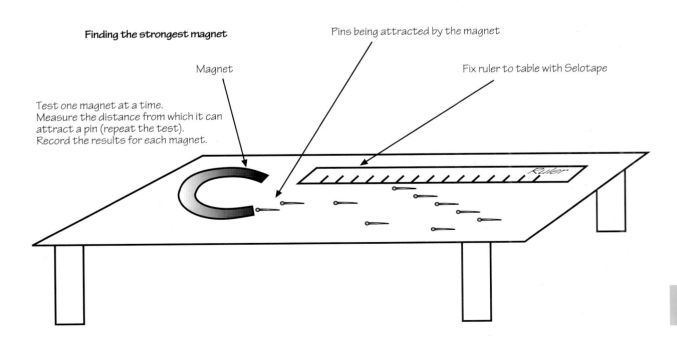

Finding the strongest magnet

Magnet

Pins being attracted by the magnet

Fix ruler to table with Selotape

Test one magnet at a time.
Measure the distance from which it can attract a pin (repeat the test).
Record the results for each magnet.

First activities

1 Safety first

Discuss the dangers associated with electricity and how accidents can easily happen. To reinforce this, get the children to make posters emphasising normal safety procedures.

2 Simple circuits

Demonstrate how a light bulb lights by using a battery with two flexible terminals to complete a circuit correctly. Get the children to explain how it works. Their explanations may be simple but need to be accurate: *"the black bit goes on the little one, the big bit goes on the lines bit"*.

3 Mega light bulb

Give the children enlarging lenses, light bulbs, pencils, large pieces of white paper, rulers and colours. Ask them to make large careful observational drawings of the light bulb, showing all the details.

Learning objectives

- Electricity can be generated.
- Electricity can be used to help us.
- Electricity needs to be treated with respect to ensure safety.
- Some materials are good conductors and some are poor conductors of electricity.

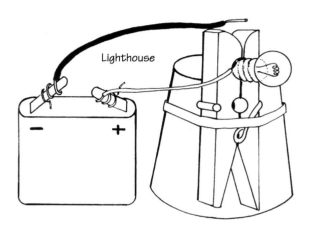

Lighthouse

4 Circuit diagrams

Make up a few different circuits using bulbs, batteries, wires, buzzers and switches. Let the children sketch these and then produce circuit diagrams for each of them.

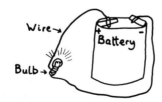

Wire →
Battery
Bulb →

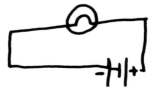

electricity

safety tools bulbs switches power

Further activities

1 Good conductors?

Make a collection of resources including a carrot, a big nail, a pencil, felt tip pen, jumbo paper clip and a pair of sunglasses. You will also need some wire, crocodile clips, electrical screwdriver, screw terminal, battery, bulb holder and a bulb or buzzer. The children should predict which objects will conduct electricity to complete a circuit and light the bulb or sound the buzzer. They should record the predictions, test each object, record the results and draw conclusions.

2 Jumbo batteries and jumbo bulbs

Using scrap materials, get the children to make large models of a light bulb and battery connecting the two so that they will light. The details of the filament and screw thread should be included.

3 Lighthouse

Get the children to make their own lighthouse using a choice of materials from: a battery, wires, plastic pots, cloths pegs, aluminium foil, rubber bands, bulbs, bulb holders and cardboard tubes. Get them to fix the wires so that the bulb is always on, invent a switch to turn the bulb on and off and also arrange it so that it flashes.

4 Not so bright

Get the children to use a bulb, bulb holder, wires and battery to light up the bulb in the normal way. Now give them some more bulbs and holders, additional wire and batteries and ask them to make a circuit in which the bulb(s) will be less bright than in the first circuit and another circuit in which the bulbs will be brighter than in the first circuit. If their circuit includes two or more bulbs in holders ask them what will happen when one of the bulbs is removed from its holder.

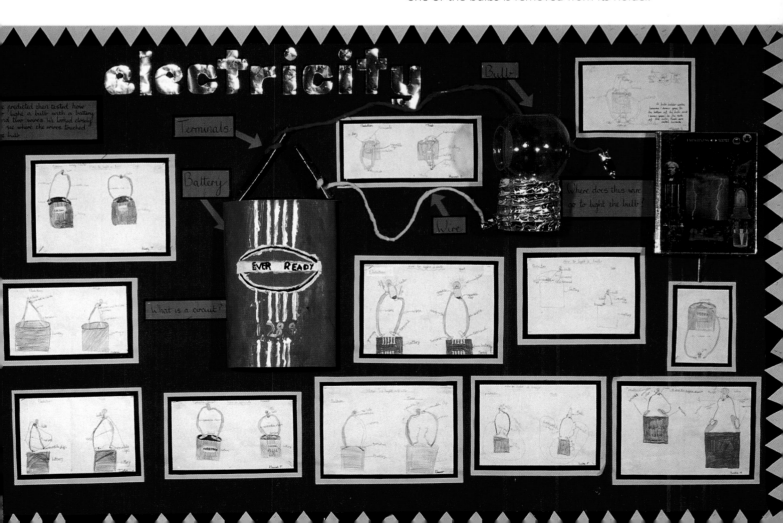

First activities

1 Sounds

Discuss with children how the voice can make different sounds and that by shaping the mouth differently we can imitate the sounds of different animals. Listen to sound effect recordings of animal cries. Prepare some flash cards with words for sounds: *shout, whisper, hiss, hum, scream, buzz, cluck, blow, laugh, cry, whistle*. Get the children to match the sounds with the words as you hold the cards up. Play a recording of *Peter and the Wolf* (Prokoviev) and ask the children to make up a simple story using just sounds.

2 Sound Quiz

Make or borrow a tape of different sounds such as rain, hail, wind, birds, animals, people whispering and shouting, trains, aeroplanes, drums, cars, bells and telephones. Play them to the class and ask them to identify each one.

Learning objectives

- Voices can make different sounds.
- The world is full of different sounds.
- Sounds have names.
- Different types of musical instruments can produce a variety of sounds.
- Sounds can remind us of things.
- Ears can hear thousands of different sounds.
- Sounds are produced by vibrating objects.
- Sound can travel through different materials.

3 Instruments

Talk about how different instruments make different sounds by blowing, clapping, striking and shaking. Name the different sections of an orchestra and make up a display of children's labelled pictures as in the photograph. Get groups of children to use musical instruments to make up sound effects for a story that they have written.

4 Make instruments

Give the children rubber bands, a large box (for a sound-box) strings, smaller cardboard boxes, balloons, sticky tape and other scrap materials. Ask them to design and make their own musical instruments. The designs shown below include a triangular frame across which are stretched rubber bands - each producing a different note; a clapper-type instrument and an instrument made from an inflated balloon combined with a tambourine, rubber bands and string.

The Orchestra

brass

strings

percussion

woodwind

soloists

conductor

Ping-pong balls on strings

Children's musical instruments

Rubber bands stretched across a triangular sound-box

Balloon fixed to tambourine

sound

Further activities

1 Sound portrait

When you organise a school trip, take a portable cassette recorder and extension microphone. During the trip, get the children to be absolutely quiet and to listen to the sounds around them e.g. bird songs, gently flowing or splashing water, the soft sound of leaves blowing in the wind, trains in the distance, aeroplanes taking off, the crack of twigs and dry leaves. Help the children to record sounds which are evocative of the environment. Paint pictures representing the sounds and make poems. When back at school, give a performance of the sounds as a portrait of the place visited.

2 Sound travels

Talk about how sound travels through different materials. Walk around the school with the children and find some things which could transmit sound, for example metal railings, wooden fencing, grass and the concrete or Tarmac playground. Ask the children to work in pairs and to send simple signals to their partners which should be repeated to confirm that the signal has been heard. Find out which materials are best by measuring the maximum distances travelled.

3 Sound search

Photocopy the illustration and ask the children to find the words that are to do with sound or music.

L	O	W	P	I	T	C	H	O	W	P	I	T	C
H	I	G	H	P	I	T	C	H	C	O	R	N	S
D	O	U	B	L	E	B	A	S	S	P	O	L	T
P	G	S	T	C	T	R	O	M	B	O	N	E	R
S	U	A	S	Y	T	E	S	U	V	T	E	N	I
T	I	R	Y	M	D	N	E	S	I	U	C	O	N
R	T	V	I	B	R	A	T	I	O	N	S	H	G
I	A	E	W	A	U	I	O	I	T	E	H	P	A
N	R	L	O	L	M	T	N	E	E	O	B	O	E
G	F	S	O	S	F	S	E	U	G	A	R	X	A
E	L	E	C	T	R	I	C	G	U	I	T	A	R
D	U	M	I	C	R	O	P	H	O	N	E	S	A
N	T	O	K	E	Y	B	O	A	R	D	T	T	M
R	E	S	T	R	T	N	P	I	A	N	O	U	E

Words included: Vibrations, Electric guitar, Cymbals, Notes, Tone, Drum, Double bass, Keyboard, Piano, Microphone, Flute, Saxophone, Trombone, Oboe, Tune, Maraca, High pitch, Low pitch, Stringed, Guitar.

Light and dark

First activities

1 Night and day

Talk about how colours look different by night and day. Ask the children to choose whether to do a picture of their house during the day or at night. Try to have equal number of children doing night and day drawings. Talk about the way the moon changes over the month and how the position of the sun appears to move in the sky. Mount the pictures on contrasting coloured paper as in the photograph.

2 Transparent

Introduce words such as *transparent, translucent* and *opaque* and link them to easy to understand definitions e.g.*translucent:* some thing you can see through not very clearly. Give the children four or five different materials (black polythene, bottle of coloured water, piece of wood, a china plate and tracing paper) to test for transparency, as in the illustration.

3 Light list

Get the children to make an illustrated list of different sources of light, natural and made, such as those shown below. Stress the fact that it is very dangerous to look directly at the sun.

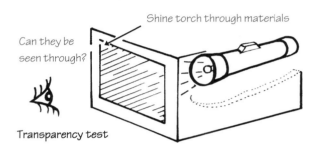

Transparency test

Further activities

1 What is the time?

Paint a large sun and mount it on the wall as in the photograph. Talk about sun dials, shadows and angles. Children can choose what kind of sun dial to make, but once the models are complete, you position them as part of a display and the children then have to paint in the shadows that would be cast by the sun.

2 Class camera

Make your classroom lightproof. Then make a small round hole by one of the windows in the blackout material. Place a large piece of white paper directly in line with the hole and move it backwards and forwards until a sharp inverted image is produced on the paper. This is best on a sunny day.

3 Make a periscope

Give the children some pieces of safety mirror and small cardboard boxes to make periscopes.

Learning objectives

- Light can be natural or man made.
- Light passes through some materials.
- Light can change direction.
- Darkness is the absence of light.
- Shadows are formed by the absence of light.
- Colours are produced when light is reflected by objects.
- Objects are seen when light enters the eye.
- Colours have names.

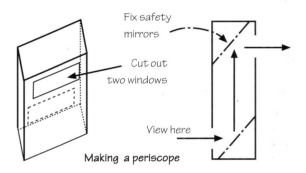

Fix safety mirrors

Cut out two windows

View here

Making a periscope

Colour and light

First activities

1 Rainbow colours

Discuss with the children how rainbows are formed and what the names of the colours of the rainbow are. Give them some paints and help them to paint their own rainbows which they could then cut out and hang as a mobile. Work on colours can be extended by adding white to colour and making tones.

2 Colour spinners

Cut some circles of card as shown in the illustration and make a hole in the centre. Paint patterns either radiating from the centre of the circle in wedges or as concentric circles. Spin the *Newton's Disk* to see colour effects.

3 Starry night

Show Van Gogh's pictures of starlit nights. Get the children to make their own light from space pictures.

4 Saturn's rings

Tie circles of cotton so that when dipped in dye a pattern of concentric rings is formed. To do this, you need to hold the centre point of the circle, pleat the fabric around and tie tightly.

5 Rainbow display

Start with indigo to make a colour theme display. Change the colour every week until all the rainbow colours have been used. Label the colours.

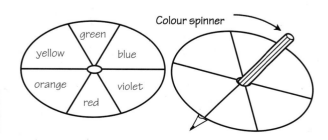

Colour spinner

Do you know the colours of the rainbow?

Further activities

1 Chromatography

Take a piece of filter paper, fold it in four, then open out to form a shallow valley in the centre. Place it on a yoghurt pot, drop one drop of colour (food colours are good) in the centre. Place a few drops of water onto the colour, allow the constituent colours to separate and when dry display as in the photograph on the opposite page.

2 Which view do you prefer?

Give the children pieces of A3 white cartridge paper and paints. Divide the class into two, one group can paint typical English landscapes, while the other group can paint an Egyptian desert or an alien landscape. Cut the finished paintings into strips and mount them on to triangular sections as in the three photographs so that the images change according to the viewer's position.

3 Moving pictures

Get the class to research into moving picture machines such as zoescopes and kaleidoscopes. Using old round biscuit tins, cardboard and safety mirrors, let children experiment and make their own moving machines.

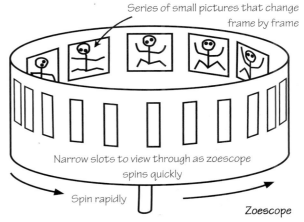

Series of small pictures that change frame by frame

Narrow slots to view through as zoescope spins quickly

Spin rapidly

Zoescope

Earth and beyond -

First activities

1 Bunny planet

Read the *Voyage to the Bunny Planet* by Rosemary Wells (Collins 1992). Get the children to make their own pictures of Janet the Bunny Queen and to help paint a large feature as in the photograph.

2 Does the sun move?

Lead the discussion about the fact that the position of the sun appears to move over the whole day. Make a large wall picture of the view from a south facing window. Follow the path of the sun throughout the day, painting it in position on the picture at 9am, 12 noon and 2.30pm.

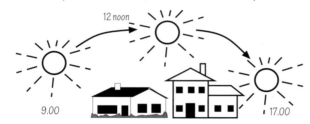

Learning objectives

- The sun appears to move across the sky.
- The earth goes around the sun.
- At different times of the year days are longer or shorter.
- The earth was formed millions of years ago.
- The earth is only one of many planets.
- There are nine planets in our solar system and they all have names.

3 Space batik

Using a piece of cotton and water based wax get the children to make a space design. Immerse the cotton in a series of dye baths containing different colours. Remove the wax and reapply until the batik is complete.

4 Moon picture

Use silver paper and non-toxic metallic paints to produce moon pictures complete with craters.

planets

Mercury | Venus | Earth | Mars | Jupiter | Saturn | Uranus | Neptune | Pluto

My Very Easy Method Just Speeds Up Naming Planets

Further activities

1   Sky at night
Use a *Helios* planetarium as shown front left in the photograph above to produce a projected image of the sky at night. To do this, use a small white walled dark room. In the centre, on the table, place the planetarium. Remove the cover and then the coloured sun sphere revealing a clear light bulb. Replace the clear plastic dome and switch on the power. The sky at night will be projected over the ceiling and walls of the room.

2   Planet names
Teach the children the memory aid (illustrated above) which will ensure they remember all the planets in the solar system. The initial letters introduce the planet names.

3   Planet origins
Get the class to research into the meanings and origins of the names of planets, making up illustrated information sheets.

71

Earth and beyond - creation

Introducton

Talk about the various creation stories and explain in a simple way how some scientists believe that everything was created with a 'big bang'. The creation stories can develop to include ideas about how the species developed and the differences between scientific theories and religious ideas. The activities suggested here combine scientific and religious accounts.

First activities

1 The 'Big Bang'

Talk about the big bang theory and ask the children to make some explosion images by using strongly coloured wax crayons on cartridge paper which is then flooded with black ink to produce vibrant impressions (see below). Mount these with the children's writings about the big bang on a black backgrounds.

The Creation.

2 The Creation

Read the biblical account of the Creation and make a class wall hanging from individual pupils' contributions. These can be butterflies, little fish, drops of rain or crumpled crepe paper to form a rainbow as shown in the photograph.

Further activities

1 Class creation book

Make a book about creation stories including these: The Rainbow Serpent, The Banyan Tree, The Sea of Milk, How the Stars got into the Sky. Pairs of children can work writing and illustrating a story for the book.

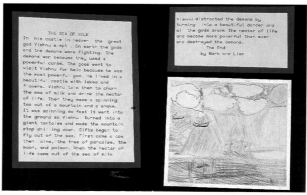

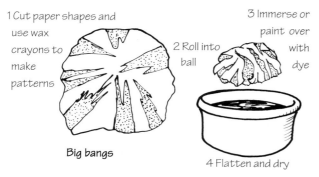

1 Cut paper shapes and use wax crayons to make patterns

2 Roll into ball

3 Immerse or paint over with dye

4 Flatten and dry

Big bangs

2 Space dictionary

Divide the class up into pairs and give each pair the task of researching one or two letters of the alphabet for space words. Write the vocabulary and illustrate it. Try to find (or make) an attractive paper to cover your space dictionary as shown in the photograph.

3 The planets

Play *The Planets* by Gustav Holst and ask the children to find words to describe their impressions of the planets. Write the most expressive phrases and words on labels and include these in individual portraits of the planets such as Jupiter in the photograph.

Dictionary entry

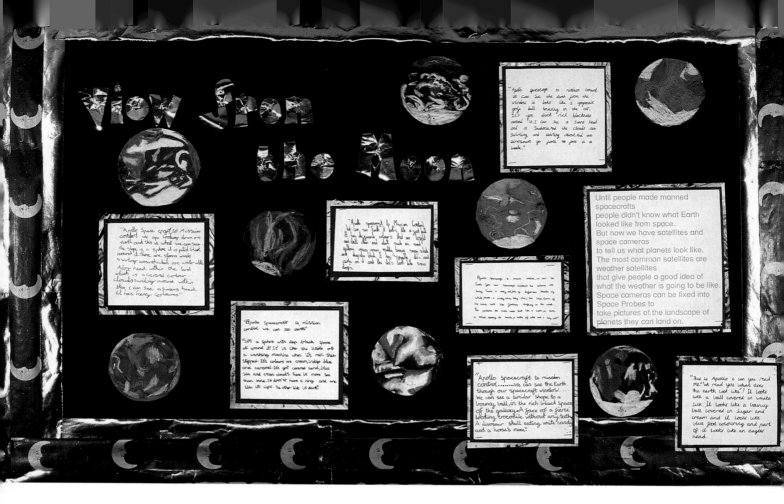

Activities

1 View from the moon

Use reference books to make careful diagrams of how the earth looks from the moon to accompany an account of the Apollo missions.

2 Space vehicle

Get the children to choose materials that will be suitable for a hostile space environment and to design and make a model that can cross different terrain.

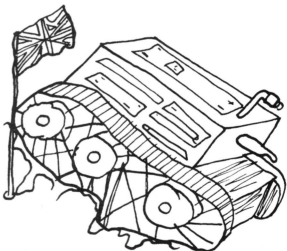

Space vehicles

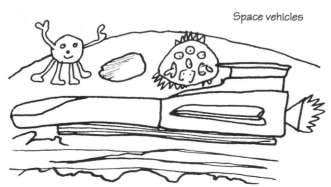

The magnetic rocket (left) is held up by identical poles on the magnetic track and the ship pushed by rocket power it is the fastest thing on the moon. The land cruiser (top) is a slow but safe means of transport heavily armoured, this cruiser will take anything you can throw at it, even a crash!

3 D'ya wanna dance?

The children could have a theme party based on space. As part of the party activities, the children are asked to design and make special space outfits for the party. They have to decide which materials to use, get some samples and choose colours if they wish to die the fabrics. Link the design activity with music and play the Beach Boys' song: *D'ya wanna dance?* The photograph shows some designs.

4 Space party

Space cakes are an important part of the space party. Children have to design attractive looking cakes, list their ingredients and recipes and draw pictures of the decorated cakes. Make the cakes which children taste, and evaluate them (see photograph)

Earth and beyond -

Introduction

The next four pages contain a range of ideas and activities for a whole school project. They link scientific knowledge with imagination and interpretation. Every child is an explorer, leaving earth to find out how animals and plants live on the strange planet Phobos (Greek for *fear*). It is necessary for the teachers to spend some time setting up the environment of Phobos - using the whole school if possible - to be full of interest, evidence and mystery. Then set the task for all the pupils:

"You are to go forth and seek out evidence of plant, animal and insect life, past and present, on this unexplored planet. I need reports, photographs, drawings of your findings."

Activities

1 Space suits and the space trip

Ask the children to imagine some of the dangers of travelling through space and landing on an unknown planet. Would there be strange space storms? Would basic life processes be supported by the conditions on the planet? In order to survive this journey to Phobos, children will need to design special space suits. Use reference books and make a list of protective measures that are needed (see photograph left).

2 Landing on Phobos

Get children to write and illustrate their account of the journey and landing on the planet, as in the photograph above, and make an expedition diary.

3 Evidence from Phobos

Draw, photograph and write about what the planet looks like.

project Phobos

Within the image:
- We created a creature that we thought would come out of the shiny egg.
- We called this creature Dinty Donty
- We all drew a picture of the creature that we had created and coloured them in pencil crayons.
- We described how and where we found the strange space eggs.
- We composed our own music to show how the creature moved and what it sounded like

4 Strange eggs

Tell the children that there are some strange eggs on Phobos and they should find them before they hatch. When they have found them they should describe how and where they were found. Draw pictures of the eggs and bring them into the spaceship for further investigation.

5 'Dinty Donty' space creature

Three strange eggs have been found on the planet Phobos by young astronauts (children). Ask them to draw what they think the creature will look like when it emerges from the egg. Make up a collage of 'Dinty Donty' as above. As an extension discuss how the creature might move and what it might sound like. Ask the children to compose and perform their own music to express the creature's movements and sounds.

77

Earth and beyond -

Life cycles from Earth and Phobos.

These are some models of insects that we thought might be found on the planet Phobos.

First activities

1 Animal life cycles from earth and Phobos

Use reference books to make illustrated diagrams of life cycles of butterflies and some other insects found on earth. Compare these with the imaginary insects found on Phobos. Make some models of the imaginary insects using all kinds of scrap materials. The photograph shows a variety of creatures made by young and older children.

2 Space fossils

Get the children to make some clay 'fossils' that were found on Phobos as evidence of previous life forms.

3 Insect sounds and anatomy

Inside the spaceship get the children to listen to sounds of insects. Open up a dead insect found on Phobos, drawing and describing in words its inside.

project Phobos

Further activities

1 Pictures of Phobos

Send some children on an imaginary exploration of the surface of Phobos and ask them to paint pictures as evidence.

2 Plant life on the planet Phobos

Tell the children to look out for signs of plant life, in particular to look for plants and seeds. Once the seeds have been found, get the astronauts to grow some in their laboratory. First they should make drawings of the plants giving information about the seeds used (weight and size) and then, as the plant grows, about the length of the stem, leaves and any similarities found with earth plants. The children are to make a model (using plaster of Paris and scrap materials) of the space plant complete with fruit, flowers, stems, leaves and roots (see photograph).

3 Crater model

Using the pictures from Activity 1, make a model of the cratered surface using plaster of Paris, fabrics and paint. Label the model to show where various scientific activities took place.

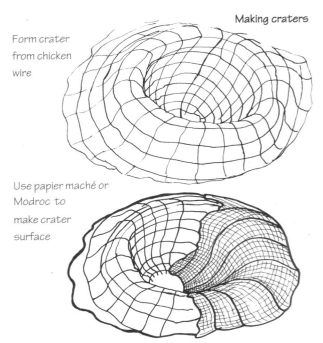

Making craters

Form crater from chicken wire

Use papier maché or Modroc to make crater surface

79

PRIMARY COLOURS — the series grows!

Primary Colours is a new series of display books packed with practical ideas and techniques to brighten up your classroom. Exciting and creative, each book provides:

- hundreds of thoroughly tried and tested curriculum ideas linked to exciting displays
- masses of colour photographs of authentic children's work to inspire your teaching
- step-by-step line drawings that explain techniques simply and clearly with at-a-glance access to ideas and resources

We're continually adding to the series with more bright, stimulating books, all clearly illustrated and explained, covering a wide range of aspects of display. If you would like to be kept up-dated with information on all our latest Primary Colours titles, simply complete the photocopiable form below and return it to us.

Brilliant books to bring added colour and sparkle to your classroom!

Books may be bought by credit card, and information obtained, by calling 01242 577944 or 01242 228888.

Photocopiable information request form

Please send me information on the latest titles in the PRIMARY COLOURS series.
Mr/Mrs/Miss/Ms ....
Address ....
.... Postcode ....
Please also send information on PRIMARY COLOURS to:
Mr/Mrs/Miss/Ms ....
Address ....
.... Postcode ....
To: Customer Services Dept., Stanley Thornes Ltd., FREEPOST (GR 782), Cheltenham, GL50 1BR

First published in 1996 by:
Stanley Thornes (Publishers) Ltd
Ellenborough House
Wellington Street
CHELTENHAM GL50 1YW
England

96 97 98 99 00 / 10 9 8 7 6 5 4 3 2 1

A catalogue record for this book is available from the British Library

ISBN 0-7487-2480-X

Printed and bound in Hong Kong by Dah Hua Printing Co., Hong Kong

Typeset by Aetos Ltd; Tadwick, Bath, Avon.